Developing Literacy
SENTENCE LEVEL

SENTENCE-LEVEL ACTIVITIES FOR THE LITERACY HOUR

year

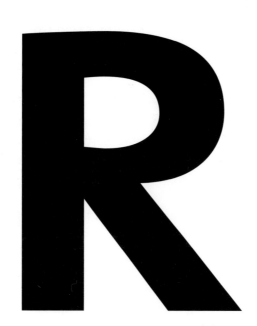

R

Christine Moorcroft

Series consultant:
Ray Barker

A & C BLACK

Reprinted 1999, 2001, 2002 (twice), 2004, 2006
Published 1999 by
A & C Black Publishers Limited
38 Soho Square, London W1D 3HB
www.acblack.com

ISBN-10: O-7136-5175-X
ISBN-13: 978-0-7136-5175-1

The authors and publisher would like to thank Ray Barker and
the following teachers for their advice in producing this
series of books: Tracy Adam; Hardip Channa; Lydia Hunt;
Madeleine Madden; Helen Mason; Yvonne Newman;
Hilary Walden; Fleur Whatley; Annette Wilson.

A CIP catalogue record for this book is
available from the British Library.

A & C Black uses paper produced with elemental chlorine-free pulp,
harvested from managed sustainable forests.

Printed in Great Britain by
St Edmundsbury Press Ltd, Bury St Edmunds, Suffolk.

Contents

Introduction

Developing Literacy: Sentence Level supports the teaching of reading and writing by providing a series of activities to develop children's understanding of the way in which the structure of sentences conveys meaning. The activities help the children to understand that a sentence can be grammatically correct even if its meaning is nonsense, for example, 'The cat sat on the mat' and 'The mat sat on the cat' are both grammatically correct, but the latter does not make sense because mats do not sit. The activities help to show the children the importance of the order of words in a sentence, and to examine the effect of changing it.

The children also learn to examine the effect of their choice of words and to question whether it communicates what they intend. They find out how their choices affect the listener or reader.

The activities are designed to be carried out in the time allocated to independent work during the Literacy Hour and therefore should be relatively 'teacher-free'; an adult will need to read some of the instructions with the children in the youngest age-groups, but many of the activity sheets have similar formats and instructions with which the children will soon become familiar.

The activities presented in **Developing Literacy: Sentence Level** support the learning objectives of the National Literacy Strategy at sentence level.

Year R helps children to develop:

- an ability to make sense of text;
- grammatical awareness;
- skills in predicting words;
- an understanding of elements of grammar –
    - capital letters
    - full stops
    - the personal pronoun 'I'
    - names;
- an understanding of different kinds of sentences and their structure, and the roles of different kinds of words.

Words from the high-frequency lists in the National Literacy Strategy *Framework for Teaching* are incorporated.

Year R promotes the development of children's understanding of the ways in which sentences are constructed and the roles of the words and punctuation marks in them. The children learn, for example, not only that there are words which denote 'doing' but also that they can not be removed from a sentence. They are encouraged to investigate the effects of changing the word-order of a sentence. Investigation is given greater emphasis as the series progresses towards Year 6.

To help pupils to work independently, the activities are presented in ways which are consistent so that even the youngest children will recognise what they have to do. They incorporate strategies which encourage independent learning – for example, ways in which children can check their own work or that of a partner.

Extension

Most of the activity sheets end with a challenge (**Now try this!**) which reinforces and extends the children's learning and provides the teacher with an opportunity for assessment.

These more challenging activities might be appropriate for only a few children; it is not expected that the whole class should complete them.

On some pages there is space for the children to complete the extension activities, but for others they will need a notebook or separate sheet of paper.

Organisation

For many of the activities it will be useful to have available scissors, glue, wooden blocks (with which to make large dice), word-banks, and a variety of dictionaries and reference books. Several activities can be re-used to provide more practice in sentence-construction, by masking words and replacing them with others.

To help teachers to select appropriate learning experiences for their pupils, the activities are grouped into sections within each book. The pages are not intended to be presented in the order in which they appear in the books, unless otherwise stated.

Structure of the Literacy Hour

The following chart shows an example of the way in which an activity from this book can be used to help achieve the required organisation of the Literacy Hour.

The hungry snail (page 28)

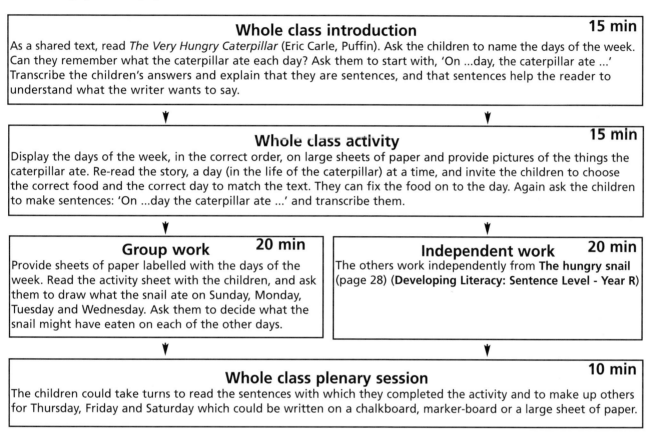

Whole class introduction   **15 min**

As a shared text, read *The Very Hungry Caterpillar* (Eric Carle, Puffin). Ask the children to name the days of the week. Can they remember what the caterpillar ate each day? Ask them to start with, 'On ...day, the caterpillar ate ...' Transcribe the children's answers and explain that they are sentences, and that sentences help the reader to understand what the writer wants to say.

Whole class activity   **15 min**

Display the days of the week, in the correct order, on large sheets of paper and provide pictures of the things the caterpillar ate. Re-read the story, a day (in the life of the caterpillar) at a time, and invite the children to choose the correct food and the correct day to match the text. They can fix the food on to the day. Again ask the children to make sentences: 'On ...day the caterpillar ate ...' and transcribe them.

Group work   **20 min**

Provide sheets of paper labelled with the days of the week. Read the activity sheet with the children, and ask them to draw what the snail ate on Sunday, Monday, Tuesday and Wednesday. Ask them to decide what the snail might have eaten on each of the other days.

Independent work   **20 min**

The others work independently from **The hungry snail** (page 28) (**Developing Literacy: Sentence Level - Year R**)

Whole class plenary session   **10 min**

The children could take turns to read the sentences with which they completed the activity and to make up others for Thursday, Friday and Saturday which could be written on a chalkboard, marker-board or a large sheet of paper.

Teachers' notes

Brief notes are provided at the bottom of most pages. They give ideas and suggestions for making the most of the activity sheet. They sometimes make suggestions for the whole-class introduction, the plenary session or, possibly, for follow-up work using an adapted version of the activity sheet. These notes could be masked before copying.

Using the activity sheets

The direction of text

This section introduces the word 'sentence' which appears on most of the activity sheets. Teachers could ask the children to point to a word on a page and to follow a sentence with a finger, stopping when they reach the end of it (the full stop). It helps the children to learn that sentences should be read from left to right (some signs and notices are written vertically, but these usually consist of only one or two words; for example, signs on some bus stops, taxi ranks and car parks). The extension activities are intended to challenge the more able readers; it is not expected that all the children will be able to attempt them.

Read and copy, **Sentence trains** and **Sentence snakes** (pages 9-11) encourage the children to read sentences from left to right, and to begin writing them (as well as reading them) on the left-side of a page.

Encourage the children to use a finger to follow lines of shared text from left to right. Ask them to point out on a large sheet of paper or blackboard where you should begin writing a sentence. Help them to get into the habit of asking themselves the question 'Where shall I begin?' before they start a piece of writing; they could remind themselves to begin on the left by marking (faintly) a tiny cross there. **Read and copy** (page 9) requires the children only to copy the sentences with the emphasis on starting in the right place and writing from left to right. **Sentence trains** and **Sentence snakes** (pages 10 and 11) add the challenge of putting in place a word which is not in its correct place.

Checking for sense

This section helps to develop the children's understanding that text should make sense, and that if it does not they have read it wrongly. It encourages them to work out what the words they can not read *might* say, by thinking about what would make sense in that context.

Making sense 1, 2, 3 and **4** (pages 12-15) help to develop accuracy in reading text by encouraging the children to check whether or not what they have read makes sense; if it does not, they should re-read it, looking more carefully at the words and, if they are not able to read them, working out what they might say which *would* make sense (and which would begin with the same initial phoneme). This strategy can be adopted during all their reading.

Writing simple sentences

The activities in this section provide structures and word-banks which help the children to construct their own simple sentences about familiar topics. Many of them can be used in shared and guided reading, with the teacher as scribe. There are also activities which teachers might find useful to support the children's work in other subjects, especially science.

All about me (page 16) makes use of words which are likely to be familiar to the children in the writing of simple sentences about themselves and the things they like. The word 'sentence' is used for a group of words which makes sense. The activity can also be used to support work in science or personal and social education. Words which are used to describe people can be written on a class 'word-wall' or word-bank.

I like (page 17) could also support work in personal and social education, particularly the development of self-esteem. The words for the foods and drinks are likely to be familiar to most children, despite the difficult spellings of some of them. During the introductory session the children could listen to groups of words and say whether or not they are sentences: for example, 'I like a', 'I like beans', 'I toast' and 'I like'.

I can (page 18), like the previous two activities, could support work in the development of self-esteem, as the children select from the labelled pictures one thing in each group which they can do. They copy the familiar word to complete a simple sentence. During the introductory session the children could listen to groups of words and say whether or not they are sentences: for example, 'I can hopping', 'I can dinner and 'I can'.

The frog, **The worm** and **The poppy** (pages 19-21) introduce the style of non-fiction texts which contain diagrams. The children have to use the text from the diagram as well as from a supplementary text box to complete simple sentences about a frog, a worm and a poppy respectively. The activities also develop their skills in using non-fiction texts to answer questions. These activity sheets could be used to support work in science, and they could be used as a pattern for the teacher to make similar sheets about other living things. They also consolidate the children's knowledge of high-frequency words: this, the, is, has and a.

Hot things (page 22) follows a similar pattern to the previous sheets in the section: the children complete simple sentences which have the same structure with familiar easy-to-read words. This activity sheet encourages the children to use the skills learned in the Literacy Hour to help them to research scientific questions.

Toys (page 23), like the previous activities in this section, provides simple sentences using high-frequency words (I, play, with, a) which the children complete with words for toys which are given on the page. This time progressively fewer words are provided in each sentence. The children should read what they have written to check it for sense: for example, if they have not noticed the absence of the word 'with' in the third sentence, they might have a sentence which reads 'I play a top'.

The weather (page 24) shows familiar symbols used on school weather charts. It introduces the skill of interpreting charts and it could be used to support work in geography. As in the previous activities in the section, the children complete simple sentences with words given on the page, with progressively fewer words being provided for them each time. They should read the sentences they have written, checking them for sense.

In the country (page 25), like **The frog**, **The worm** and **The poppy** (pages 19-21), makes use of labels. This activity can be linked with work in geography in which the children learn the names of common features. Again they are asked to complete simple sentences (this time beginning with 'I can see') in which progressively fewer words are provided for them. As in the previous activity, the children should read the sentences they have written, checking them for sense.

Robot (page 26) provides an opportunity for introducing the children to capital letters which begin sentences. They could begin by looking for the word which begins each sentence. There is also an opportunity for the children to learn that a sentence ends with a full stop. When they have made their sentences from the cut-out words, they could check that each one ends with a full stop. With an adult, the children could play games in which they listen to a piece of text being read and call 'Stop!' when the reader comes to the end of a sentence.

Robot kit (page 27) has an emphasis on reading: the children need to read and make sense of the information given on the activity sheet in order to colour the robot correctly. This activity provides an opportunity to use the skills developed during the Literacy Hour to support work in mathematics, as the children follow simple instructions which require them to count and to consider different attributes of the robot.

The hungry snail (page 28) requires the children to work with more complex sentences, but the format of the activity will be familiar if they first read (as a shared reading activity) *The Very Hungry Caterpillar* by Eric Carle (Puffin) in which the caterpillar eats something different every day and in which the days of the week are named. The children should read and make sense of the information supplied with the pictures and use it to help them to match the two halves of the sentences.

During the plenary session, the teacher could ask the children to read aloud the sentences they have made, while the others check them for accuracy (by referring to the activity sheet). They could make a collage of the things the hungry snail eats, alongside which their completed activity sheets could be displayed.

The fat cat (page 29) has a similar format to the previous activity: the children are required to read and make sense of the information given with the pictures and to use it to help them to match the two halves of the sentences.

Grammatical awareness

This section provides activities which develop the children's grammatical awareness by asking them to consider which words would make sense in gaps in sentences, to make up sentences using given beginnings, middles and endings and to play games which involve sentence-building. It consolidates their understanding of what a sentence is and encourages them to check that what they have read and written makes sense.

Shake a sentence 1 and 2 (pages 30 and 31) The words used in these activities are mainly from the list of high-frequency words suggested in the National Literacy Framework for this age-group, with a few other simple words. The children should be encouraged to consider whether or not the word they throw on the 'middles' die could possibly follow the one which they threw on the 'beginnings' die, for example, 'like' can not follow 'It', 'see' can not follow 'He', and so on.

In **Sentence machines 1, 2** and **3** (pages 32-34), like the previous activities, the children are required to consider which words can follow one another in a sentence and to make up very simple sentences from the words given in the 'sentence machines'. The extension activity provides an opportunity for them to make up as many sentences as they can, using combinations of the given words.

Funny sentences (pages 35-37) is designed for fun. The 'beginnings' are all subjects, the 'middles' are all verbs and the 'endings' are all adverbial phrases. The children can make up silly sentences as they play this game, which follows the rules of the game 'Consequences'. Any combination of a 'beginning', a 'middle' and an 'ending' will make sense grammatically, however silly it sounds: it will have a subject and a verb, for example, 'A fish skipped in the playground'. The children could copy and illustrate some of the funny sentences they make.

Nursery rhyme matching 1 and **2** and **Fairy-tale sentences** (pages 38-40) use texts which will be familiar to the children. Sentences from these texts are cut in two; the children have to match them. In the first activity the two parts of the sentences rhyme, which will help the children to match them. The second activity asks them to match the two parts without the help of rhyme. An extension for **Nursery rhyme matching 1** and **2** could be made by copying sentences from other nursery rhymes and cutting them in half for the children to match.

Jam tarts (page 41) provides an opportunity to work with non-fiction text, reading sentences which are instructions. It includes some text-level prediction with which the children should be able to cope if they are reminded what the recipe is for (jam tarts, although no jam has been put in yet and they have not been baked). The children should make use of the pictures to assist their reading of each instruction. The extension activity requires some text-level prediction which will provide the opportunity for the children to write two instructional sentences.

If possible (at another time), make jam tarts with the children, cut out the pictures from the recipe and ask the children to put them in the correct order.

The magic spell, Sentence mixers 1 and **Sentence mixers 2** (pages 42-44) develop the ability to write a simple sentence. The children should have no difficulty in reading the words in the examples. They need to decide with which word to begin their sentence (this is an opportunity to reinforce the idea that sentences begin with a capital letter). Some of the sentences include words which always have a capital letter, such as names and the personal pronoun 'I', but no other word in any of the examples begins with a capital letter.

When they play **Sentence dominoes** (pages 45-47), the children are required to select, from the cards they hold, a word which can be used to begin a sentence or to continue a sentence which has already been started. The activity will develop their awareness of combinations of words which make sense, and of capital letters and full stops. The teacher could encourage them to say when a sentence is complete. For this game, all three pages are needed. To make the game simpler, reduce the number of dominoes: remove some of the words for the subject of a sentence (in this game they all come at the beginning of the sentence, and so begin with a capital letter), some of the verbs, some of the words for the object of the verb (such as football and chips) and some of those which make up phrases such as 'at school', 'to the park' and 'to bed'.

Predicting

Some of the activities in this section develop the children's ability to consider the meaning of a sentence and then to predict missing words; others develop their ability to consider an incomplete sentence within the context of a small piece of text and then to predict words which can be used to complete the sentence. Some of these activities encourage the children to re-read previous sentences in order to understand the one they are reading and to complete it if words were omitted. This skill can be transferred to other texts which the children read: if they come across a word they can not read, a useful self-help strategy is to re-read the previous sentence or sentences.

Several activities in this section prepare the children for later work on grammar: their attention is implicitly drawn to different kinds of words and their functions in a sentence, although parts of speech are not named. For example, **What do they have?** (page 48) is about nouns and **Who does it?** (page 49) is about the subject of a sentence. **What do they have?** also helps the children to use the familiar sentence-opening 'I have' in their own writing. **Hide and seek** (page 50) concentrates on the word or phrase which says where the action took place. The children can analyse simple sentences if they are asked questions which help them to develop an awareness of the different parts of a sentence and their purposes.

In **Patch's day** (page 51) the children work out from the pictures what Patch is doing. The words provided (nouns preceded by 'a' or 'one') help with spellings. **In the park** (page 52) has a similar format. These two activities can be used as a pattern to help the children to write their own picture stories.

There was an old lady (page 53) is based on the well-known story-song of the old lady who swallowed a fly. The children need first to be familiar with the story so that they know the difficult words such as 'swallowed' and 'catch'. As the children carry out the activity they could remind themselves of the sequence of events by singing the song with a partner.

In **Missing middles** (page 54) and **Missing word** (pages 55-57) the children develop the skill of predicting words in sentences which helps them to approach words they find difficult. If they come to words in other texts which they can not read, they can be encouraged to consider what the word might say, by using a combination of cues: the surrounding text, the pictures (if there are any), the first sound of the word and any other sound they recognise in it.

Grammatical awareness

This introduces proper nouns (but does not use that term). The children learn that a name is an important word for a particular person or character.

My name (page 58), **Names of other children** (page 59) and **Hidden names** (page 60) concentrate on people's given names (see also **Developing Literacy: Word Level Year R**) which provides activities on writing names. The children might notice that a person's given name is not always special to one person (there might be more than one child in the class with the same name); some children might be able to cope with family names as a way to distinguish (in text) between two people with the same given name. Others might be able to take this further and consider what can be done if two or more people have the same given names and family names.

Hidden names (page 60) develops the children's ability to recognise a name among other words and to use names in sentences. They consolidate their ability to recognise capital letters (see also **Developing Literacy: Word Level Year R**).

In **Nursery rhyme names** (page 61) the names are more difficult to read than those in the previous activities, but the children should recognise them, with the help of the pictures, if they know the rhymes. After reading the rhymes to the children, repeating them and inviting the children to join in, the teacher could ask questions such as: 'Who met a pieman?' and 'Who climbed up the spout?' The children could point to the illustrations on the activity sheet as they answer. Encourage the children to check the spellings of the characters' names in nursery rhyme books.

Sorting the post (page 62) provides an example of the use of people's names to deliver the post. The children could address letters to one another and take turns to sort and deliver them. They could discuss the additional information which might be needed if letters were sent to children in other classes or even in other schools.

I (page 63) and **Using 'I'** (page 64) develop the children's ability to use the personal pronoun 'I'. The first activity concentrates on how to write the letter and shows that 'I' is a word used by anyone to refer to himself or herself. The second activity develops the children's understanding of the changes in a verb when 'I' is used instead of a name.

Glossary of terms used

adverb A word which describes or modifies a verb, for example, *quickly* or *carefully*.
adverbial phrase A phrase which expands the verb, answering the questions how? when? or where? For example, *one after the other*, *in the morning* or *in the playground*.
character A person or animal, for example, in a story, poem, play or television or radio programme.
clause A distinct part of a sentence which includes a verb; for example, *while we were playing*.
cue A source of information in reading which may be contextual, grammatical, graphic or phonological. It helps children to read unfamiliar words.
phoneme The smallest unit of sound in a word. A phoneme can be represented by one to four letters; for example, st**ay**, s**igh**t, st**eep**.
phonics The relationship between sounds and the written form of a language.
phrase Two or more words which act as one unit, for example, *in the corner*.
rhyme The use of words which have the same sound in their final syllable; for example, <u>fox</u>/<u>rocks</u>, <u>sore</u>/<u>door</u>.

Read and copy

- **Read the sentences.**
- **Copy the sentences.**

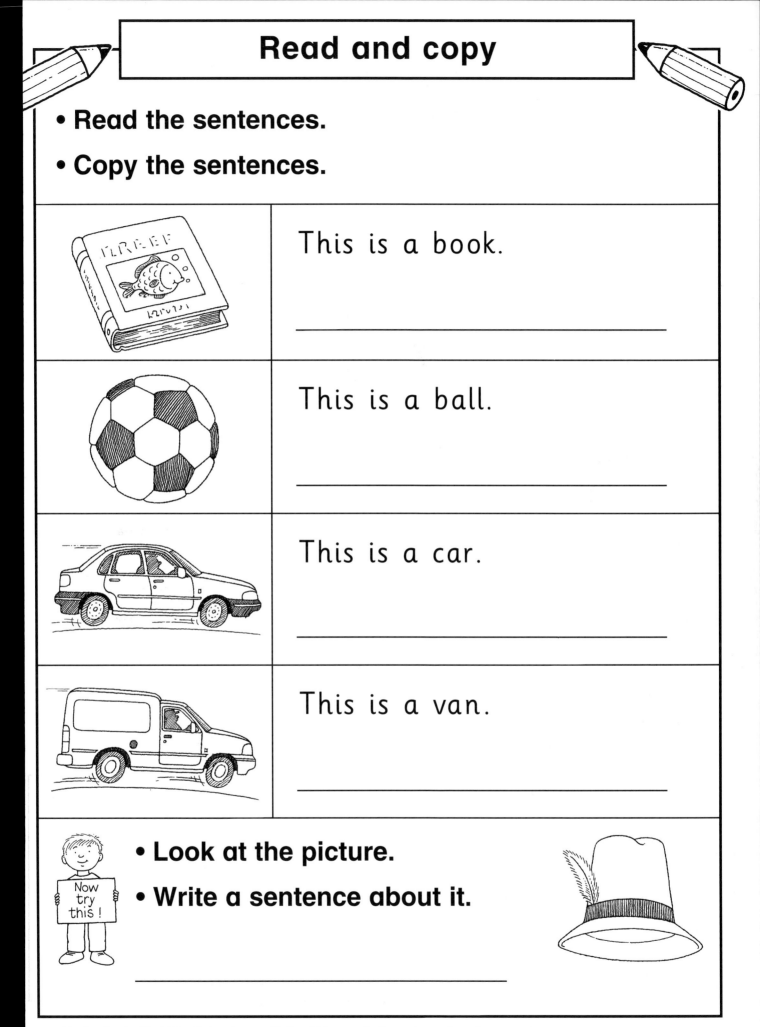

This is a book.

_____

This is a ball.

_____

This is a car.

_____

This is a van.

_____

- **Look at the picture.**
- **Write a sentence about it.**

_____

Teachers' note Model the first sentence with the children: write it on a large piece of paper and read it with them, asking them to look at the picture on their copies of the page. Invite them to come up and put a mark where they think you should begin copying the sentence.

Developing Literacy
Sentence Level Year R
© A & C Black

Sentence trains

- **Find the word which got lost.**
- **Write it in the space.**
- **Read the sentence.**
- **Copy the sentence.**

- **Draw a train.**
- **Write a sentence about the train.**

Teachers' note Point out that each sentence starts at the front of the train (on the left-hand side of the page) and ask the children to follow the sentences with a finger from left to right. Ask them to point out and read the word which is out of place.

**Developing Literacy
Sentence Level Year R
© A & C Black**

Sentence snakes

- **Find the word which got lost.**
- **Write it in the space.**
- **Read the sentence.**
- **Copy the sentence.**

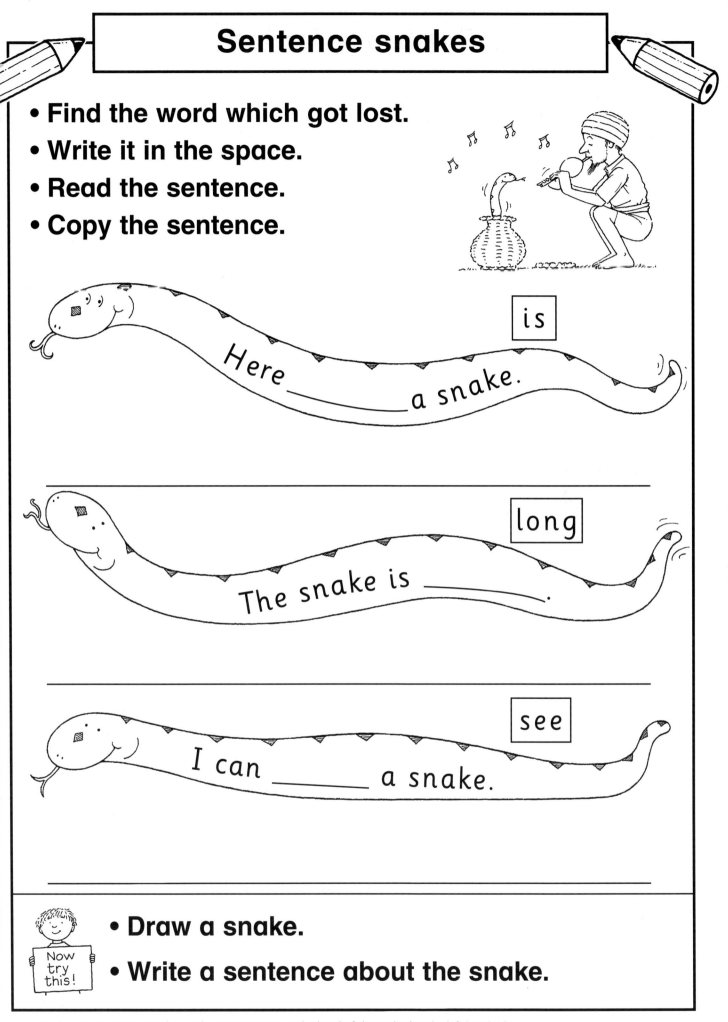

Here _____ a snake. | is |

The snake is _____ . | long |

I can _____ a snake. | see |

- **Draw a snake.**
- **Write a sentence about the snake.**

Now try this!

Teachers' note Point out that each sentence starts at the head of the snake (on the left-hand side of the page) and ask the children to follow the sentences with a finger from left to right. Ask them to point out and read the word which is out of place.

Developing Literacy
Sentence Level Year R
© A & C Black

Making sense 1

- **Read each sentence.**
- **Does it make sense?** ✓ or ✗
- **Underline the words which are different.**

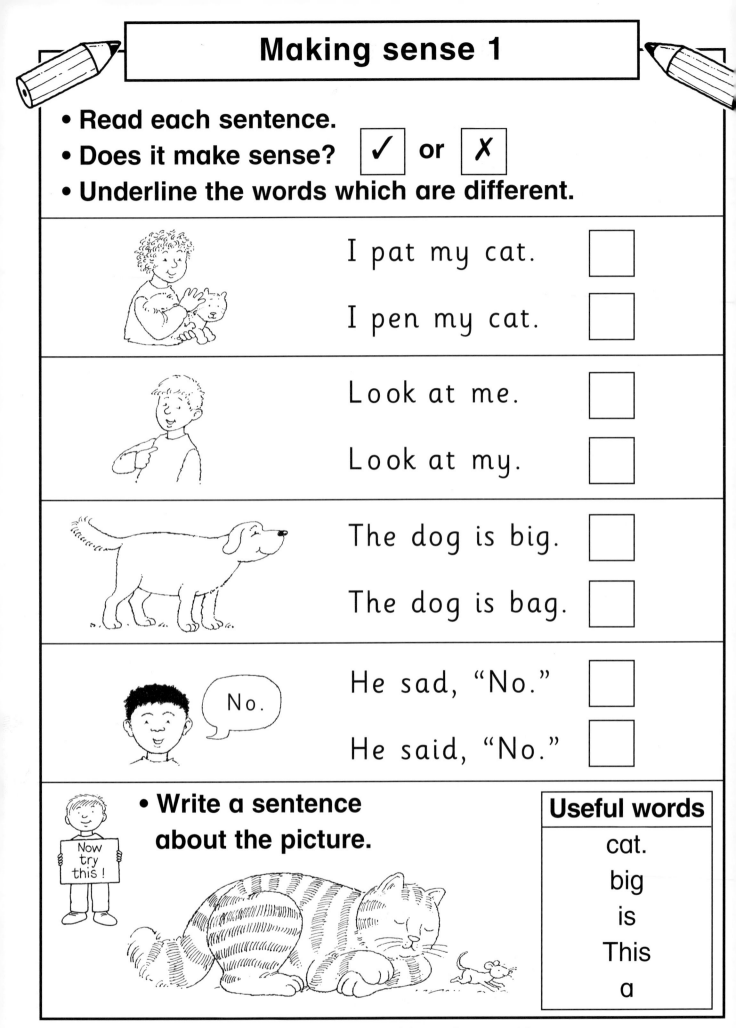

I pat my cat. ☐

I pen my cat. ☐

Look at me. ☐

Look at my. ☐

The dog is big. ☐

The dog is bag. ☐

He sad, "No." ☐

He said, "No." ☐

- **Write a sentence about the picture.**

Useful words

cat.

big

is

This

a

Teachers' note The children could work in pairs, taking turns to read the sets of sentences while the other follows the text with a finger. They could ask one another if what they have read makes sense and, when it does not, say what they think is wrong.

Developing Literacy
Sentence Level Year R
© A & C Black

Making sense 2

- **Read each sentence.**
- **Does it make sense?** ✓ or ✗
- **Underline the words which are different.**

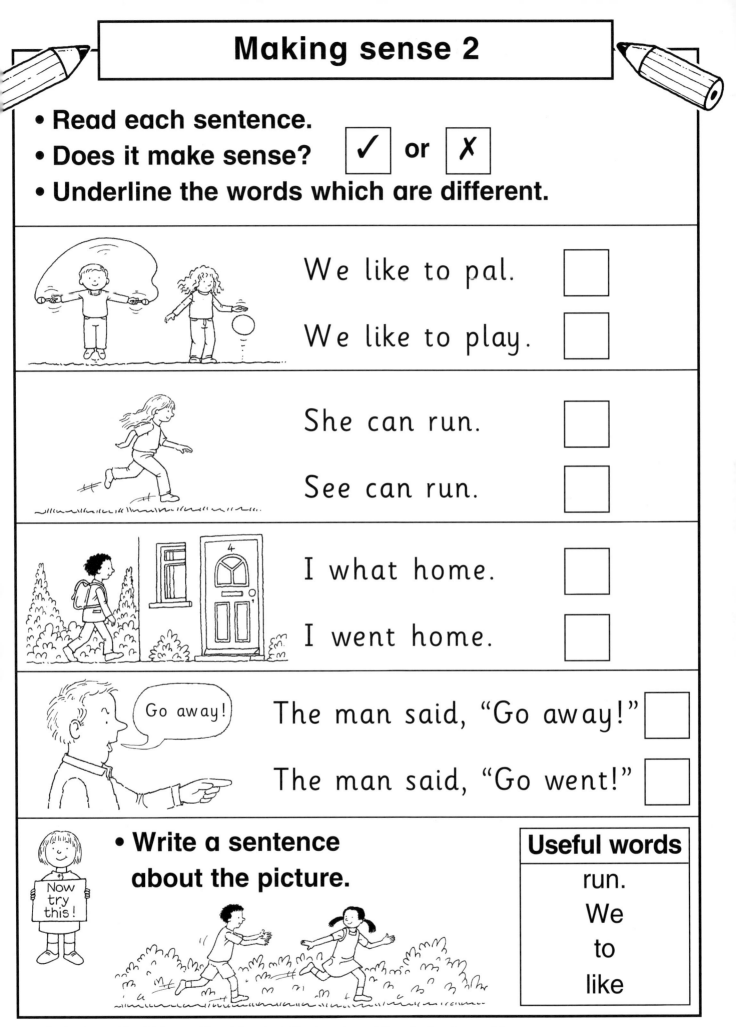

We like to pal. ☐

We like to play. ☐

She can run. ☐

See can run. ☐

I what home. ☐

I went home. ☐

The man said, "Go away!" ☐

The man said, "Go went!" ☐

- **Write a sentence about the picture.**

Useful words

run.

We

to

like

Teachers' note The children could work in pairs, taking turns to read the sets of sentences while the other follows the text with a finger. They could ask one another if what they have read makes sense and, when it does not, say what they think is wrong.

Developing Literacy
Sentence Level Year R
© A & C Black

13

Making sense 3

- **Read each sentence.**
- **Does it make sense?** ✓ **or** ✗
- **Underline the words which are different.**

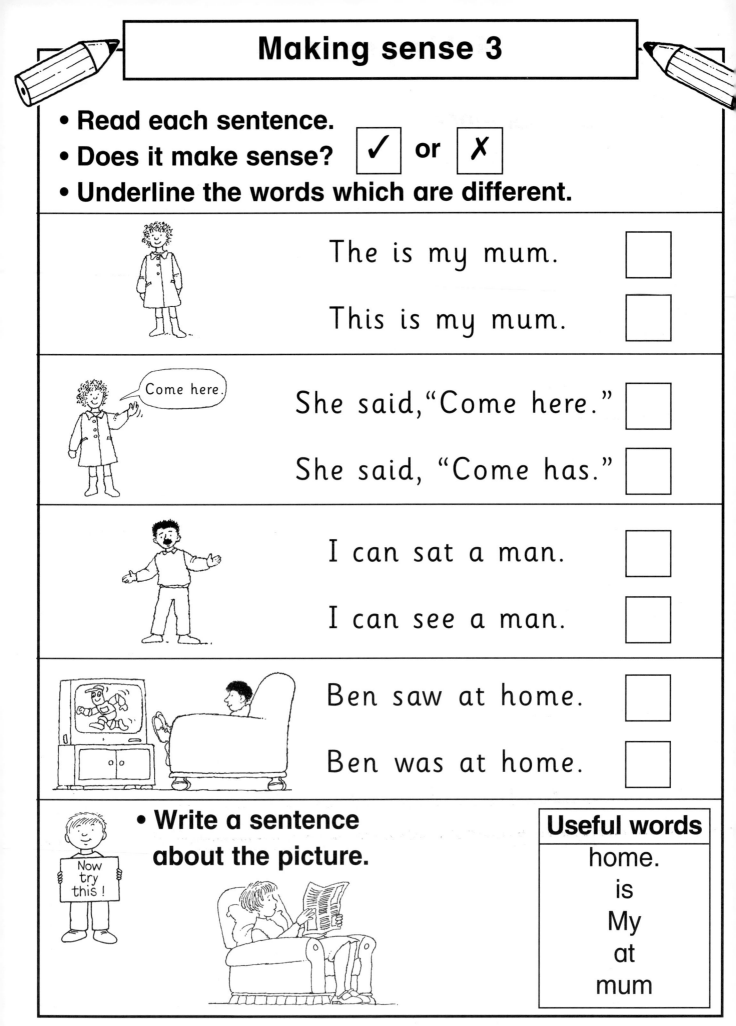

The is my mum. ☐

This is my mum. ☐

She said, "Come here." ☐

She said, "Come has." ☐

I can sat a man. ☐

I can see a man. ☐

Ben saw at home. ☐

Ben was at home. ☐

- **Write a sentence about the picture.**

Useful words

home.
is
My
at
mum

Teachers' note The children could work in pairs, taking turns to read the sets of sentences while the other follows the text with a finger. They could ask one another if what they have read makes sense and, when it does not, say what they think is wrong.

Developing Literacy
Sentence Level Year R
© A & C Black

Making sense 4

- **Read each sentence.**
- **Does it make sense?** ✓ **or** ✗
- **Underline the words which are different.**

It is a some day. ☐

It is a sunny day. ☐

I am going out. ☐

I am garden out. ☐

Here and two cats. ☐

Here are two cats. ☐

Like at my dog. ☐

Look at my dog. ☐

Now try this!

- **Write a sentence about the picture.**

Useful words	
dog	The
cat	are
out.	going
and	the

Teachers' note The children could work in pairs, taking turns to read the sets of sentences while the other follows the text with a finger. They could ask one another if what they have read makes sense and, when it does not, say what they think is wrong.

Developing Literacy
Sentence Level Year R
© A & C Black

All about me

• **Draw a picture of yourself.**

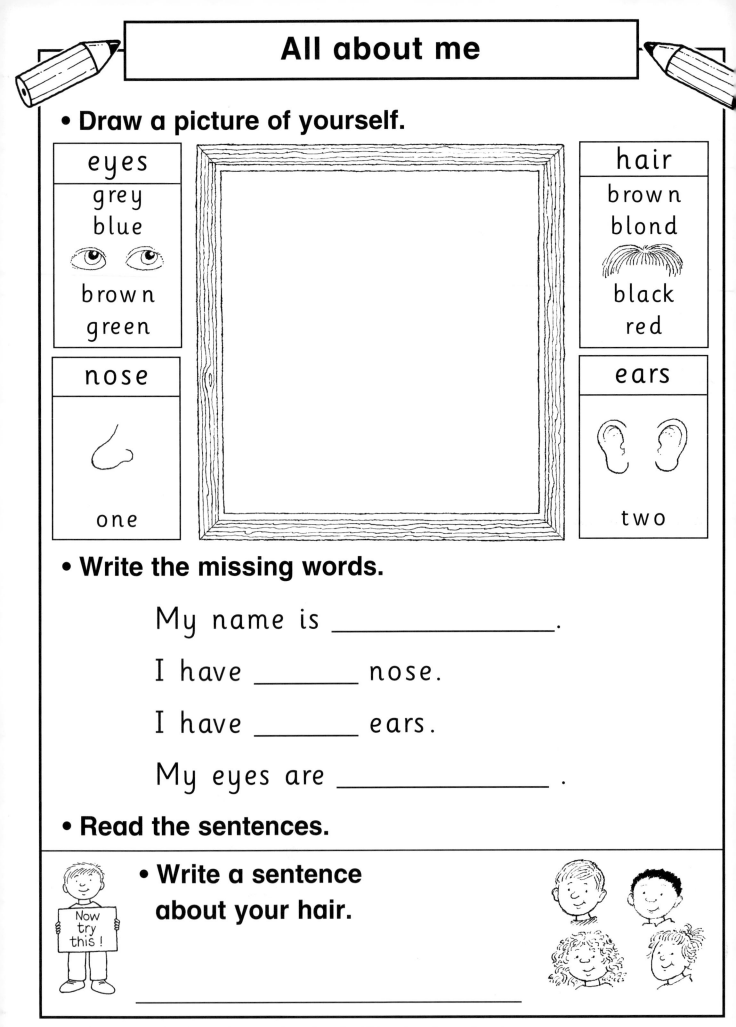

eyes

grey
blue

brown
green

nose

one

hair

brown
blond

black
red

ears

two

• **Write the missing words.**

My name is _____ .

I have _____ nose.

I have _____ ears.

My eyes are _____ .

• **Read the sentences.**

Now try this!

• **Write a sentence about your hair.**

_____

Teachers' note During the introductory session, talk to the children about the words used to describe hair and eye colours and the words for the numbers one and two.

Developing Literacy
Sentence Level Year R
© A & C Black

I like

- **What do you like?**

- **Write the missing words.**

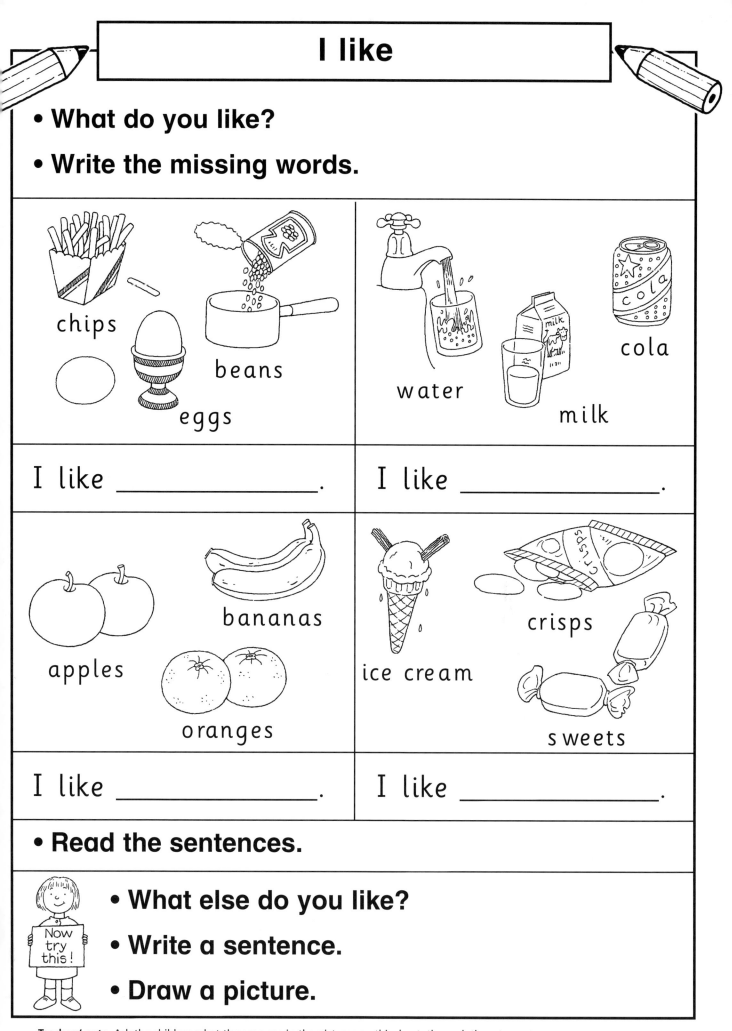

chips

beans

eggs

water

milk

cola

I like _____.

I like _____.

apples

bananas

oranges

ice cream

crisps

sweets

I like _____.

I like _____.

- **Read the sentences.**

Now try this!

- **What else do you like?**

- **Write a sentence.**

- **Draw a picture.**

Teachers' note Ask the children what they can see in the pictures on this sheet, then ask them to take turns to read a word and say whether or not it is a sentence. Point out the words below the pictures and complete the first example with them, asking whether you have made a sentence.

Developing Literacy
Sentence Level Year R
© A & C Black

I can

- **What can you do?**
- **Write the missing words.**

run

sit

read

skip

clap

walk

I can _____.

I can _____.

hop

swim

sing

jump

play

eat

I can _____.

I can _____.

- **Read the sentences.**

Now try this!

- **What else can you do?**
- **Write a sentence.**
- **Draw a picture.**

Teachers' note After completing their sentences the children could read them to a partner and compare their answers. During the plenary session the children could take turns to say a sentence which begins 'I can...'

Developing Literacy
Sentence Level Year R
© A & C Black

The frog

- **Write the missing words.**

- **Colour the picture.**

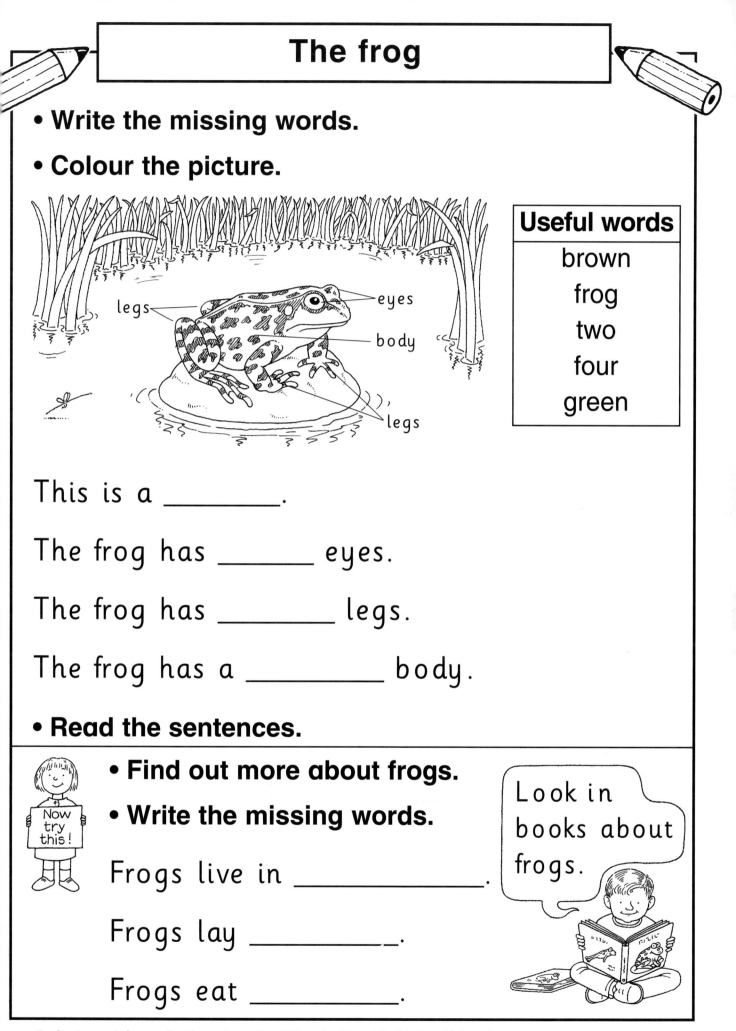

Useful words

brown
frog
two
four
green

This is a _____ .

The frog has _____ eyes.

The frog has _____ legs.

The frog has a _____ body.

- **Read the sentences.**

Now try this!

- **Find out more about frogs.**

- **Write the missing words.**

Frogs live in _____ .

Frogs lay _____ .

Frogs eat _____ .

Look in books about frogs.

Teachers' note Before reading the sentences the children should read the labels and follow the line from each label to the picture of the frog. Provide simple reference books about frogs and encourage the children to find out as much as they can from the pictures as well as the text.

Developing Literacy
Sentence Level Year R
© A & C Black

19

The worm

- **Write the missing words.**

- **Colour the picture.**

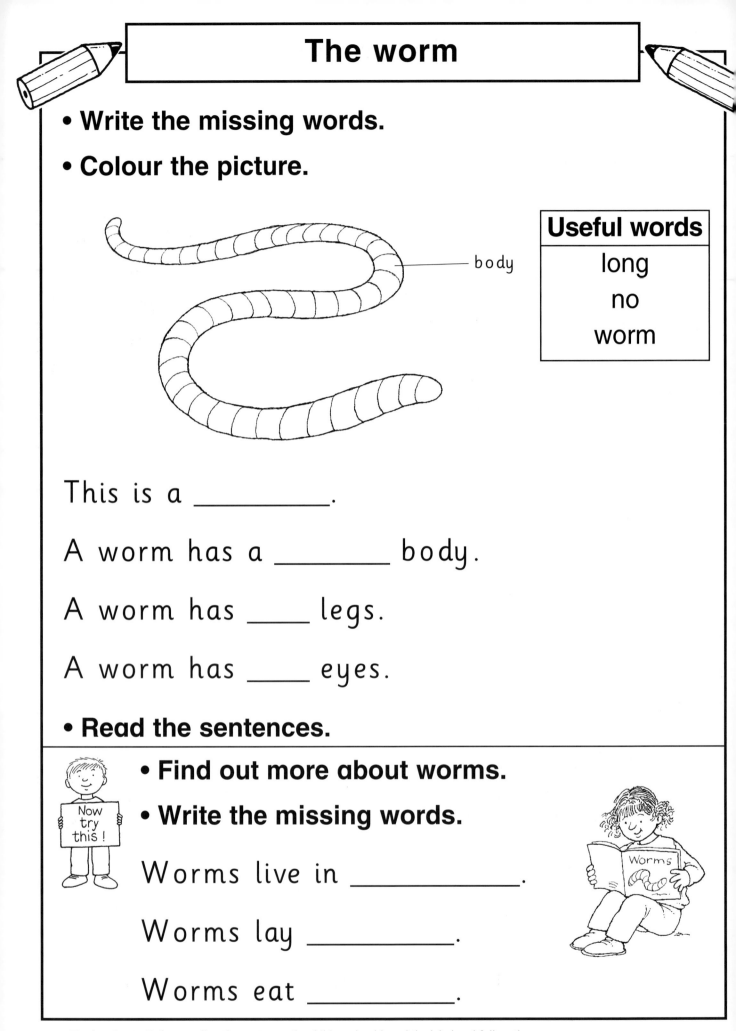

body

Useful words

long

no

worm

This is a _____.

A worm has a _____ body.

A worm has ____ legs.

A worm has ____ eyes.

- **Read the sentences.**

- **Find out more about worms.**

- **Write the missing words.**

Now try this !

Worms live in _____.

Worms lay _____.

Worms eat _____.

Teachers' note Before reading the sentences the children should read the label and follow the line from the label to the picture of the worm. Provide simple reference books about worms and encourage the children to find out as much as they can from the pictures as well as the text.

Developing Literacy
Sentence Level Year R
© A & C Black

The poppy

- **Write the missing words.**

- **Colour the picture.**

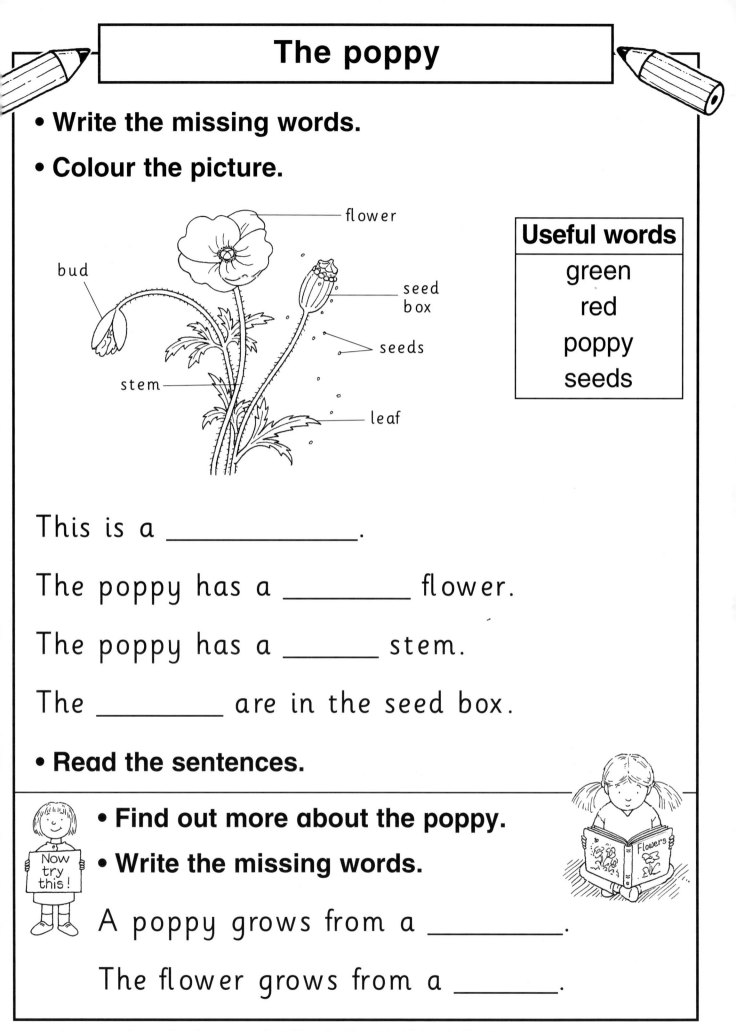

Useful words

green
red
poppy
seeds

This is a _____ .

The poppy has a _____ flower.

The poppy has a _____ stem.

The _____ are in the seed box.

- **Read the sentences.**

- **Find out more about the poppy.**

- **Write the missing words.**

A poppy grows from a _____ .

The flower grows from a _____ .

Teachers' note Before reading the sentences the children should read the labels and follow the line from each label to the picture of the poppy. Provide simple reference books about flowers and encourage the children to find out as much as they can from the pictures as well as the text.

**Developing Literacy
Sentence Level Year R
© A & C Black**

Hot things

- **Write the missing words.**
- **Read the sentences.**

a fire   a pan   the Sun

burn   hot

A fire is _____.

A pan ____ _____.

The _____ ___ _____.

Hot things can _____ you.

- **Draw two other hot things.**
- **Write sentences about them.**

Now try this!

Use a word bank or dictionary.

Teachers' note During the introductory session, show the children pictures of hot things and invite them to say a sentence about each, using the words 'hot' and 'burn'.

**Developing Literacy
Sentence Level Year R
© A & C Black**

Toys

- **Look at the pictures.**

- **Write the missing words.**

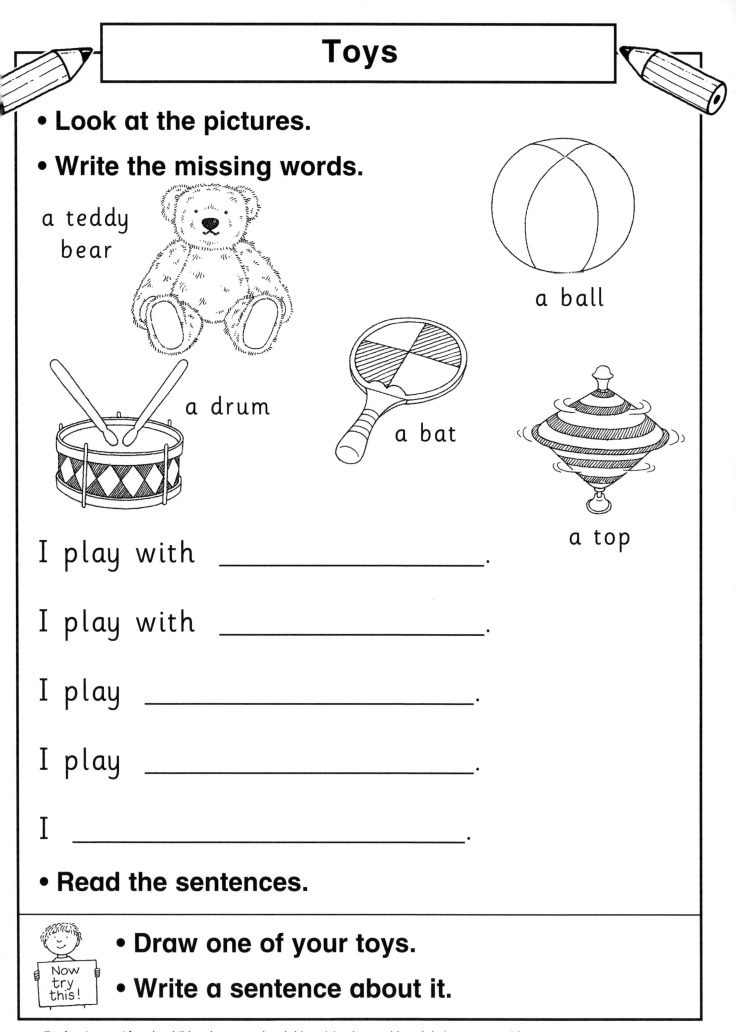

a teddy bear

a ball

a drum

a bat

a top

I play with _____.

I play with _____.

I play _____.

I play _____.

I _____.

- **Read the sentences.**

- **Draw one of your toys.**

- **Write a sentence about it.**

Teachers' note After the children have completed this activity they could read their sentences with a partner and check each one for sense. Encourage them to notice if they have missed out a word and how this affects the sense of a sentence, particularly where they have to supply more than one word.

Developing Literacy
Sentence Level Year R
© A & C Black

The weather

- **Look at the pictures.**
- **Write the missing words.**

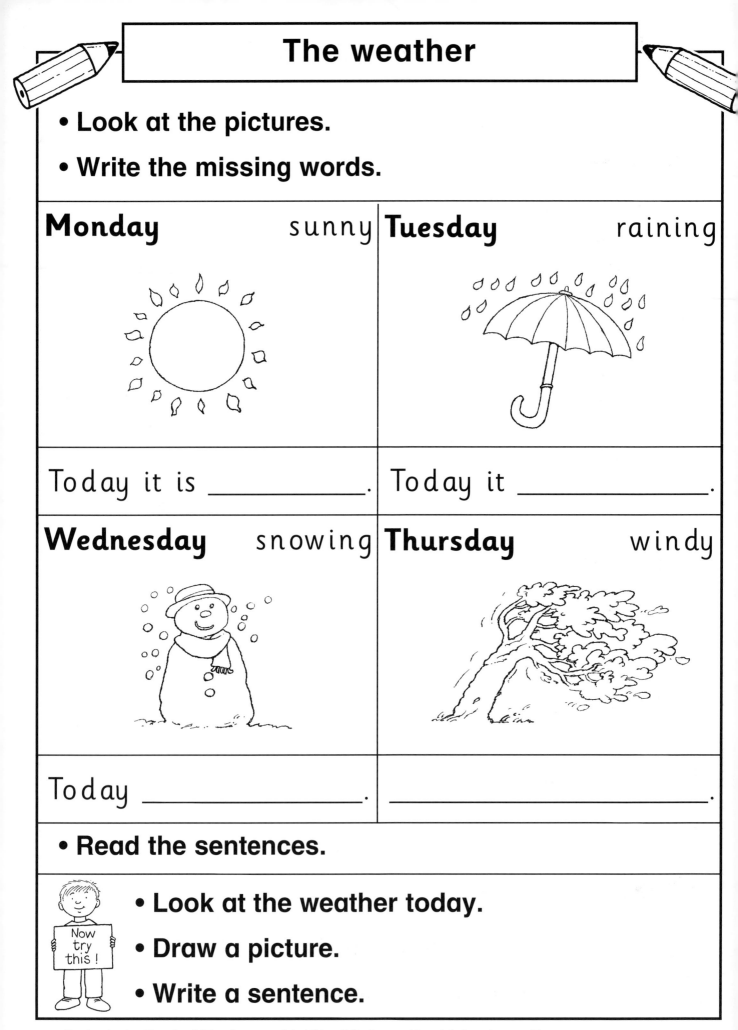

| Monday | sunny | Tuesday | raining |

Today it is _____.

Today it _____.

| Wednesday | snowing | Thursday | windy |

Today _____.

_____.

- **Read the sentences.**

- **Look at the weather today.**
- **Draw a picture.**
- **Write a sentence.**

Teachers' note After the children have completed this activity they could read their sentences with a partner and check each one for sense. Encourage them to notice if they have missed out a word and how this affects the sense of a sentence, particularly where they have to supply more than one word.

Developing Literacy
Sentence Level Year R
© A & C Black

In the country

- **Look at the picture.**

  What can you see?

- **Write the missing words.**

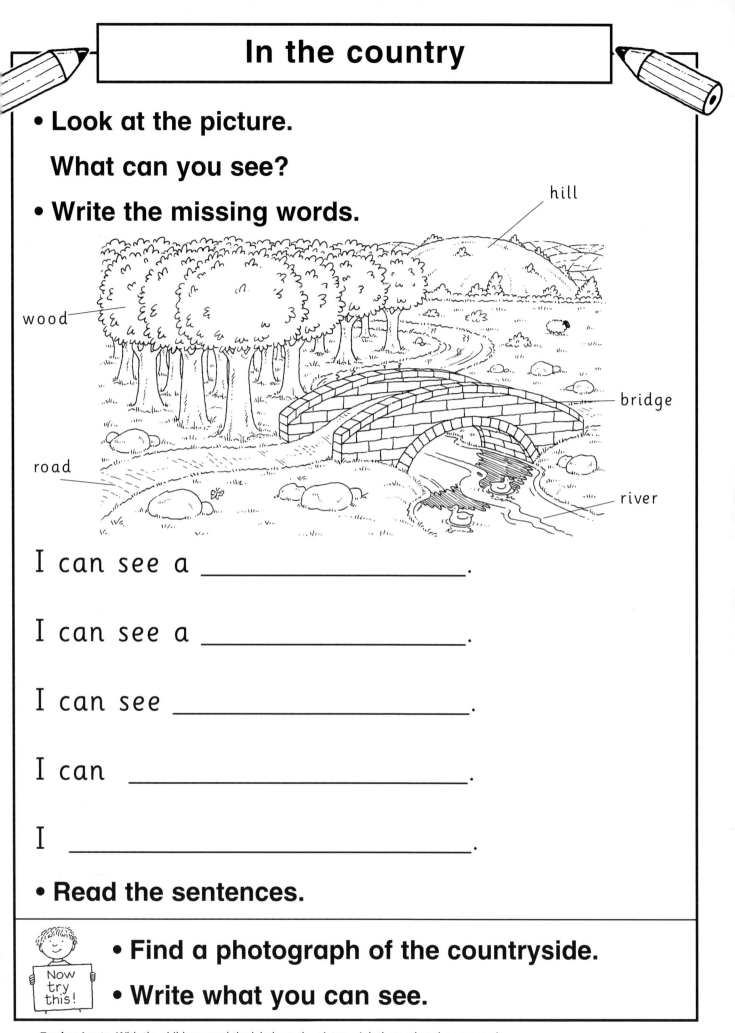

I can see a _____.

I can see a _____.

I can see _____.

I can _____.

I _____.

- **Read the sentences.**

- **Find a photograph of the countryside.**
- **Write what you can see.**

Now try this!

Teachers' note With the children, read the labels on the picture. Ask them what they can see in the picture, encouraging them to answer in sentences which begin 'I can see...'. Provide pictures of countryside scenes and help the children to compile a word bank about the countryside.

Developing Literacy
Sentence Level Year R
© A & C Black

25

Robot

- **Make sentences about the robot.**
- **Read the sentences.**

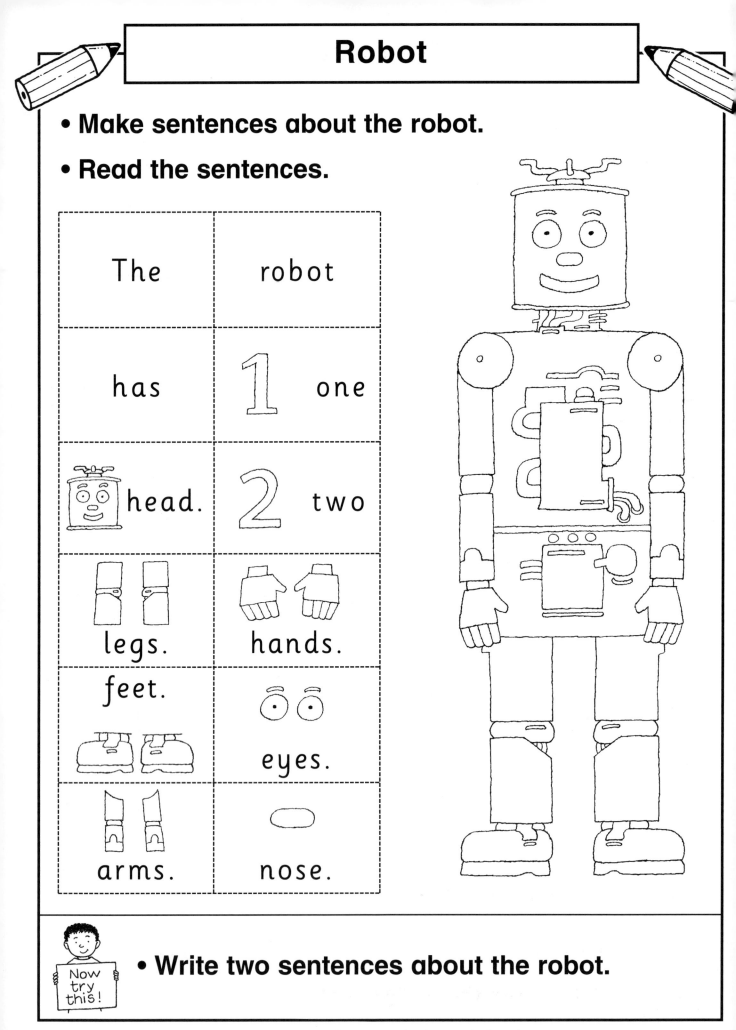

The	robot
has	1 one
head.	2 two
legs.	hands.
feet.	eyes.
arms.	nose.

- **Write two sentences about the robot.**

Now try this!

Teachers' note The children could read with a partner the sentences they have made about the robot; they could check the accuracy of one another's sentences by referring to the picture.

Developing Literacy
Sentence Level Year R
© A & C Black

Robot kit

- **Read the sentences.**
- **Colour the robot.**

The robot has red eyes.

The robot has a green nose.

The robot has a blue mouth.

The robot has black hands.

The robot has yellow feet.

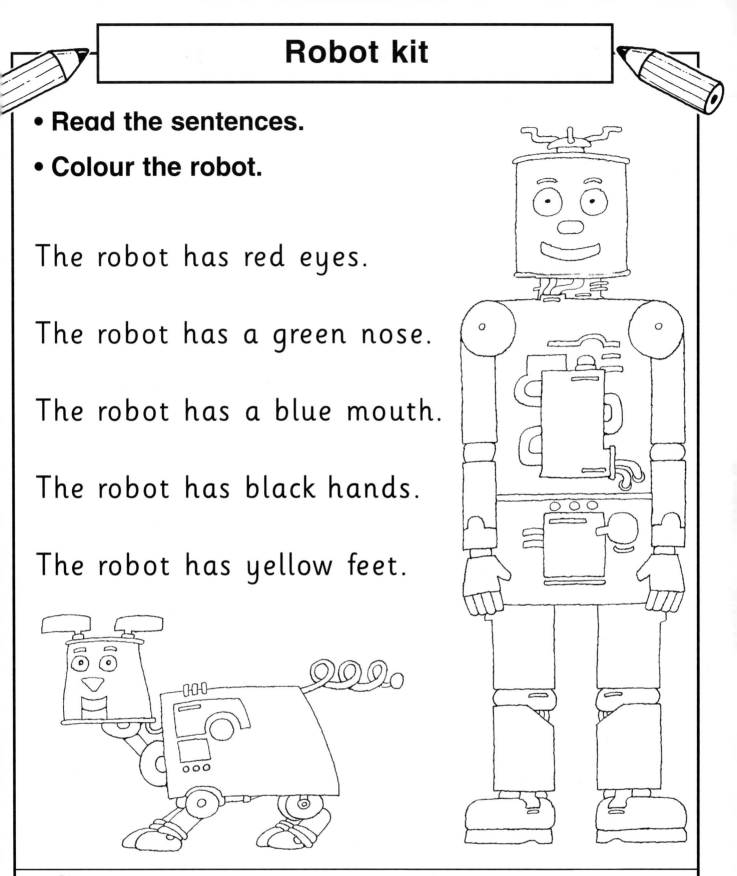

- **Draw a robot.**
- **Colour it.**
- **Write a sentence about it.**

Now try this!

Teachers' note A spare copy of the page could be made with the descriptive words masked, so that the children can colour the robot and ask a friend to complete the sentences about it.

Developing Literacy
Sentence Level Year R
© A & C Black

The hungry snail

- **Look at the pictures.**
- **Read the words.**
- **Join the leaves to make sentences.**

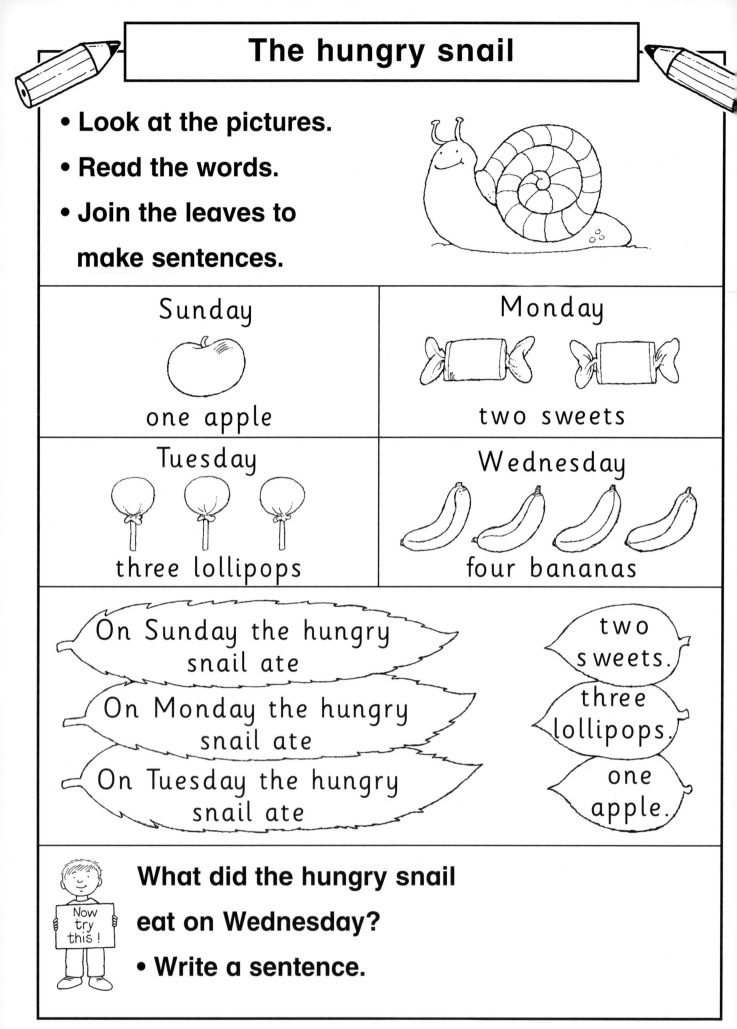

Sunday	Monday
one apple	two sweets

Tuesday	Wednesday
three lollipops	four bananas

On Sunday the hungry snail ate

On Monday the hungry snail ate

On Tuesday the hungry snail ate

two sweets.

three lollipops.

one apple.

What did the hungry snail eat on Wednesday?

- **Write a sentence.**

Now try this!

Teachers' note Additional 'leaves' could be drawn and cut out from separate pieces of paper and written on for the children to match.

Developing Literacy
Sentence Level Year R
© A & C Black

The fat cat

- **Look at the pictures.**
- **Read the words.**
- **Join the fish to make sentences.**

sat on the gate

hid in the hat

ran up the tree

played on the bed

The fat cat ran

The fat cat hid

The fat cat played

on the bed.

up the tree.

in the hat.

What else did the fat cat do?

- **Write a sentence.**

Now try this!

_____

Teachers' note After the children have completed this activity they could read the sentence they have made to a partner, who checks it for accuracy by referring to the activity sheet.

Developing Literacy
Sentence Level Year R
© A & C Black

Shake a sentence 1

- **Cut out the boxes on each strip.**
- **Glue each set of words on to a block.**

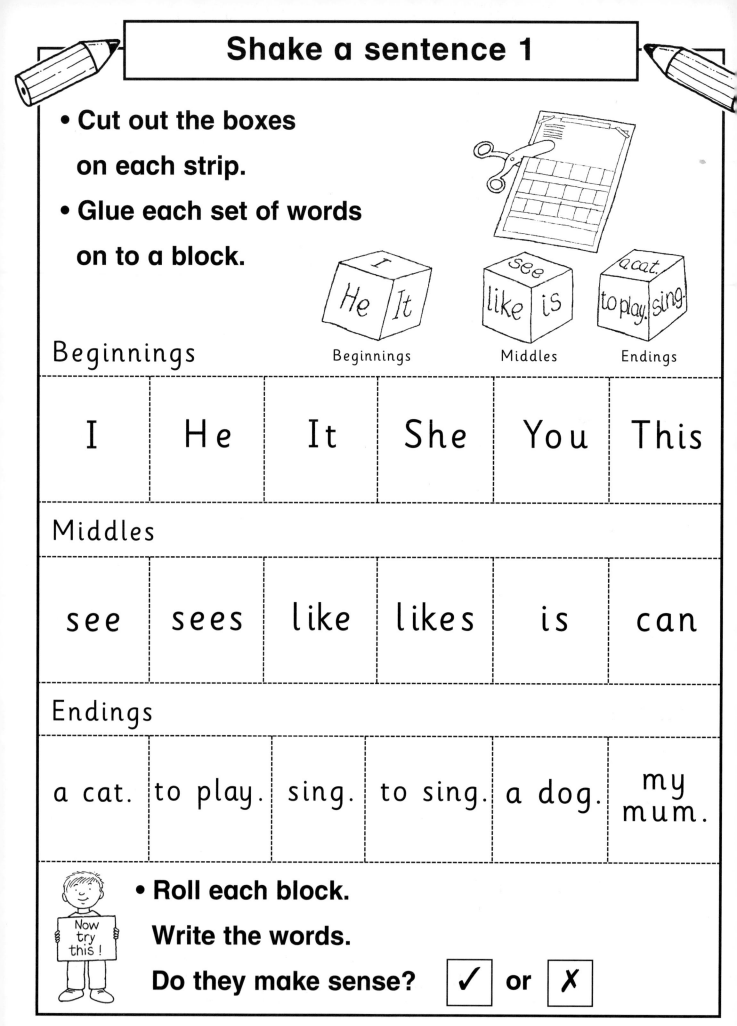

Beginnings   Middles   Endings

Beginnings

I	He	It	She	You	This

Middles

see	sees	like	likes	is	can

Endings

a cat.	to play.	sing.	to sing.	a dog.	my mum.

- **Roll each block.**

  Write the words.

  Do they make sense? ☐ ✓ or ☐ ✗

Now try this !

Teachers' note Prepare the dice as shown. The children take turns to roll each die and write the word they throw. Ask them if they have written a sentence: does it make sense? If not, what is wrong with it?

Developing Literacy
Sentence Level Year R
© A & C Black

30

Shake a sentence 2

- **Cut out the boxes on each strip.**
- **Glue each set on to a block.**

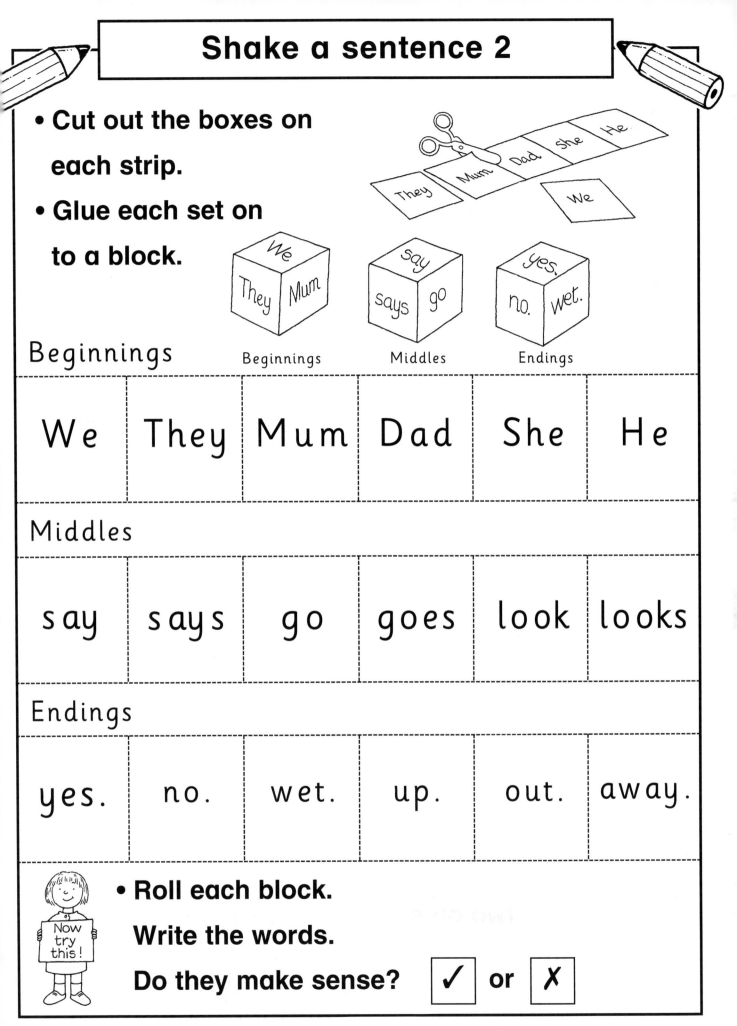

Beginnings · Middles · Endings

Beginnings

We	They	Mum	Dad	She	He

Middles

say	says	go	goes	look	looks

Endings

yes.	no.	wet.	up.	out.	away.

- **Roll each block.**

  Write the words.

  Do they make sense? ✓ or ✗

Teachers' note Prepare the dice as shown. The children take turns to roll each die and write the word they throw. Ask them if they have written a sentence: does it make sense? If not, what is wrong with it?

Developing Literacy
Sentence Level Year R
© A & C Black

Sentence machines 1

- **Choose a word from each machine.**
- **Write a sentence.**
- **Read the sentence.**

Does your sentence make sense?

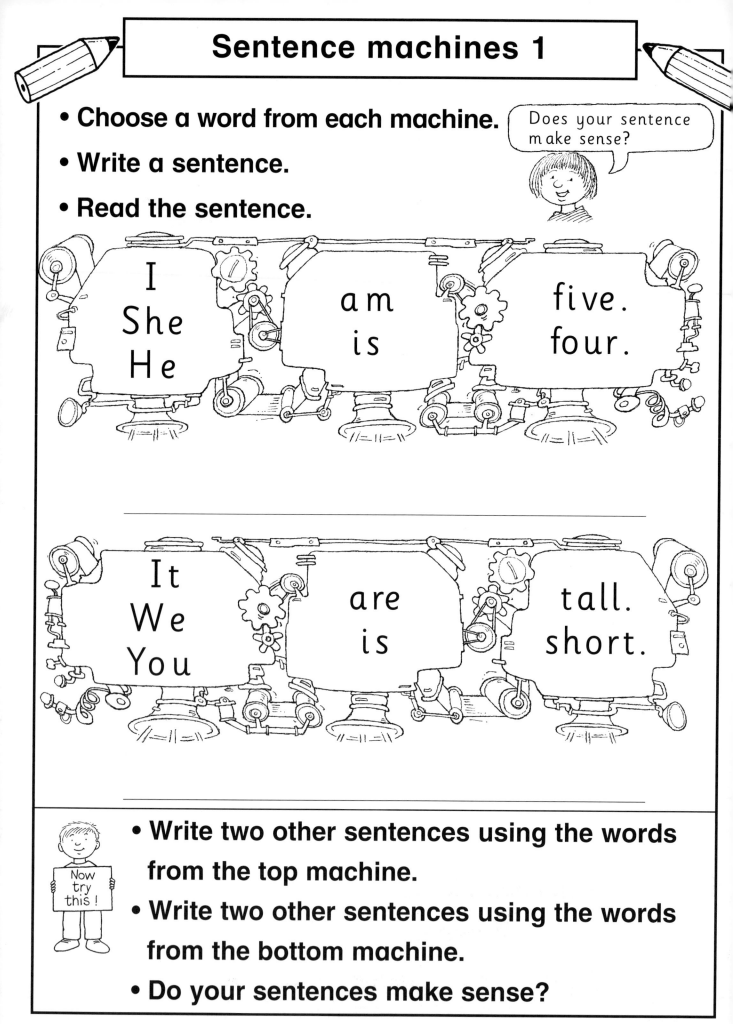

I She He

a m is

five. four.

It We You

are is

tall. short.

- **Write two other sentences using the words from the top machine.**
- **Write two other sentences using the words from the bottom machine.**
- **Do your sentences make sense?**

Now try this!

Teachers' note With the children, read the words in the machines and model a sentence which does not make sense, asking the children which word they would change so that it does make sense. During the plenary session the children could take turns to read their sentences aloud while the others check them for sense.

Developing Literacy
Sentence Level Year R
© A & C Black

Sentence machines 2

- **Choose a word from each machine.**
- **Write a sentence.**
- **Read the sentence.**

Does your sentence make sense?

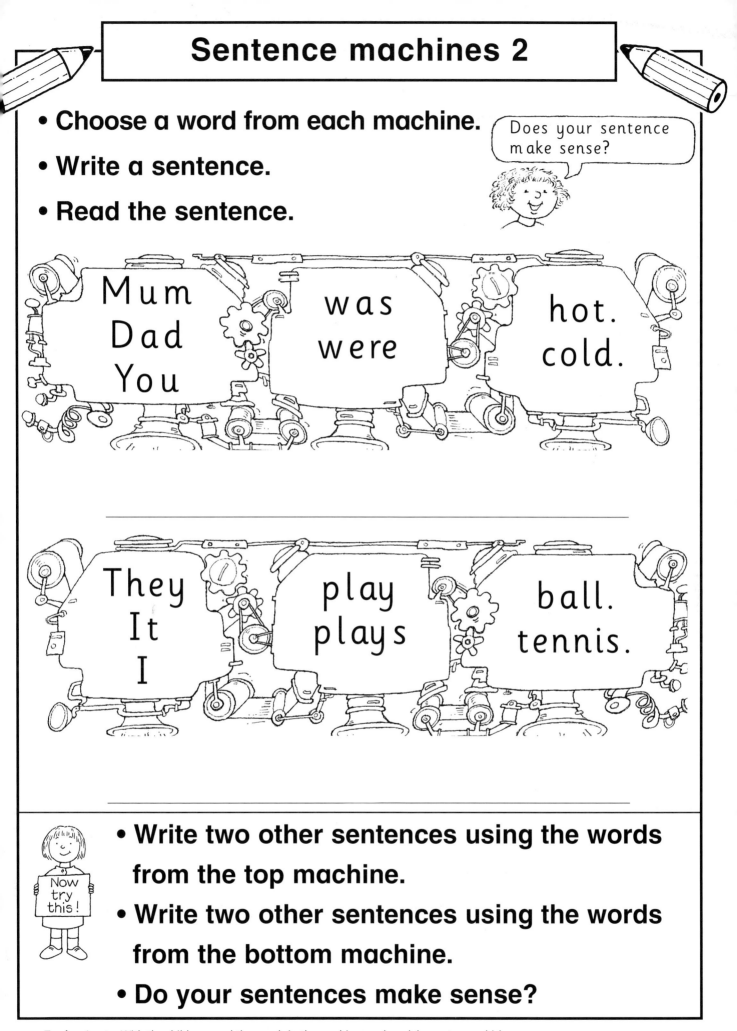

Mum Dad You

was were

hot. cold.

They It I

play plays

ball. tennis.

- **Write two other sentences using the words from the top machine.**
- **Write two other sentences using the words from the bottom machine.**
- **Do your sentences make sense?**

Now try this!

Teachers' note With the children, read the words in the machines and model a sentence which does not make sense, asking the children which word they would change so that it does make sense. During the plenary session the children could take turns to read their sentences aloud while the others check them for sense.

Developing Literacy
Sentence Level Year R
© A & C Black

33

Sentence machines 3

- **Choose a word from each machine.**
- **Write a sentence.**
- **Read the sentence.**

Does your sentence make sense?

| The It | is car was | my went her | car. fast. |

| The He | saw bike had | was a | red. bike. |

Now try this !

- **Write two other sentences using the words from sentence machine 1.**
- **Write two other sentences using the words from sentence machine 2.**
- **Do your sentences make sense?**

Teachers' note With the children, read the words in the machines and model a sentence which does not make sense, asking the children which word they would change so that it does make sense. During the plenary session the children could take turns to read their sentences aloud while the others check them for sense.

Developing Literacy
Sentence Level Year R
© A & C Black

A bird

Mum

A frog

Three dogs

A boy

A girl

A mouse

A fish

A horse

A snake

A rat

A plane

Teachers' note Photocopy pages 35-37, glue them on to card and cut them into their individual cards. Put them face down in separate piles. Each child takes a card from the 'beginnings' pile and turns it over. Continued on page 36.

Developing Literacy
Sentence Level Year R
© A & C Black

Funny sentences: middles

sang

sat

hopped

barked

played

skipped

ran

swam

jumped

slid

hid

flew

Teachers' note (Continued from page 35.) Each child takes a card from the 'middles' pile, turns it over and places it to follow his or her 'beginnings' card. Continued on page 37.

Developing Literacy
Sentence Level Year R
© A & C Black

in the tree.

on a chair.

to the pond.

in the garden.

in the bedroom.

in the playground.

up the clock.

in the sea.

in the field.

under the gate.

in a hole.

in the sky.

Teachers' note (Continued from pages 35 and 36.) Each child takes a card from the 'endings' pile, turns it over and uses it to complete his or her sentence. During the plenary session the children read their sentences to the rest of the class. The results will be grammatically correct, albeit comical.

Developing Literacy
Sentence Level Year R
© A & C Black

- **Read the beginnings.**

- **Join them to their endings.**

- **Read the sentences.**

Beginnings

Endings

Jack and Jill

Old Mother Hubbard

The Queen of Hearts

Little Miss Muffet

went to the cupboard.

sat on a tuffet.

went up the hill.

made some tarts.

- **Copy the sentences from the rhymes.**

Teachers' note During the introductory session, read the complete rhymes with the children. For the extension activity, the children could use computer printouts of suitable rhymes in large print from which they could cut sentences and then cut them in two for a partner to match.

Developing Literacy
Sentence Level Year R
© A & C Black

Nursery rhyme matching 2

- **Read the beginnings.**
- **Join them to their endings.**
- **Read the sentences.**

Beginnings

Endings

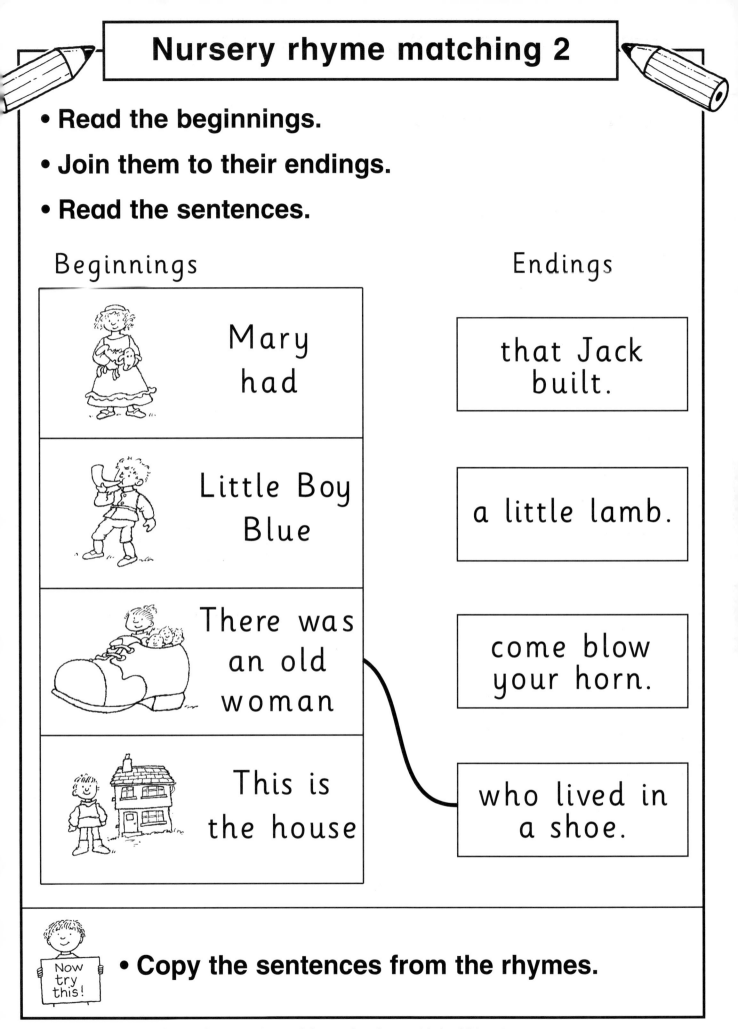

Mary had

Little Boy Blue

There was an old woman

This is the house

that Jack built.

a little lamb.

come blow your horn.

who lived in a shoe.

- **Copy the sentences from the rhymes.**

Teachers' note During the introductory session, read the complete rhymes with the children. For the extension activity, the children could use computer printouts of suitable rhymes in large print from which they could cut sentences and then cut them in two for a partner to match.

Developing Literacy
Sentence Level Year R
© A & C Black

Fairy tale sentences

- Read the beginnings.
- Find the endings.
- Write the sentences.
- Read the sentences.

Beginnings

Puss

_____.

Goldilocks

_____.

The gingerbread man

_____.

Endings

runs away.

broke Baby Bear's chair.

has some boots.

- Copy the sentences.

Teachers' note Ask the children if they know the stories shown on the activity sheet. Can they tell one another anything about them? Provide other stories from which they can copy sentences to cut in two for a partner to match.

Developing Literacy
Sentence Level Year R
© A & C Black

Jam tarts

- **Look at the pictures.**
- **Read the words.**
- **Complete the sentences.**

into the flour	water
an apron	Roll
your hands	Cut

Wash _____ .

Put on _____ .

Rub the margarine
_____ .

Mix in the _____ .

_____ out the pastry.

_____ out the tarts.

- **What will you do next?**
- **Draw the next two pictures.**
- **Write the sentences.**

Now try this!

Teachers' note Talk about the recipe, ensuring that the children know what it is for. Ask them to name all the things they would need to make jam tarts. List them. Encourage the children to look at the pictures to help them read each instruction and to use the word box to help them to complete the sentences.

Developing Literacy
Sentence Level Year R
© A & C Black

The magic spell

The fairy has cast a spell on the children. It mixes their words.

- **What are they saying?**
- **Write the sentences.**

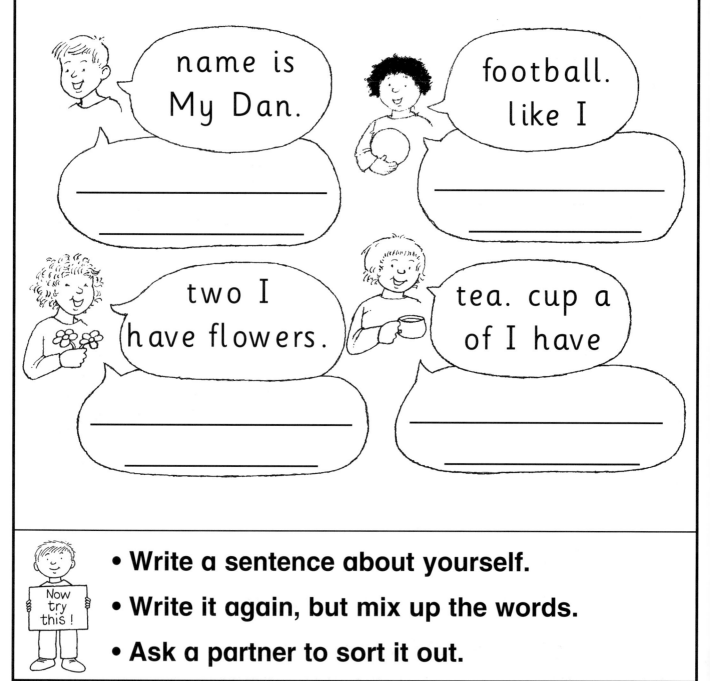

name is
My Dan.

_____

_____

football.
like I

_____

_____

two I
have flowers.

_____

_____

tea. cup a
of I have

_____

_____

- **Write a sentence about yourself.**
- **Write it again, but mix up the words.**
- **Ask a partner to sort it out.**

Now try this!

Teachers' note Model the first example with the children, helping them to find the first and last word in the sentence.

**Developing Literacy
Sentence Level Year R
© A & C Black**

Sentence mixers 1

There is a sentence in each mixer.

- **Write the sentences correctly.**

- **Read the sentences.**

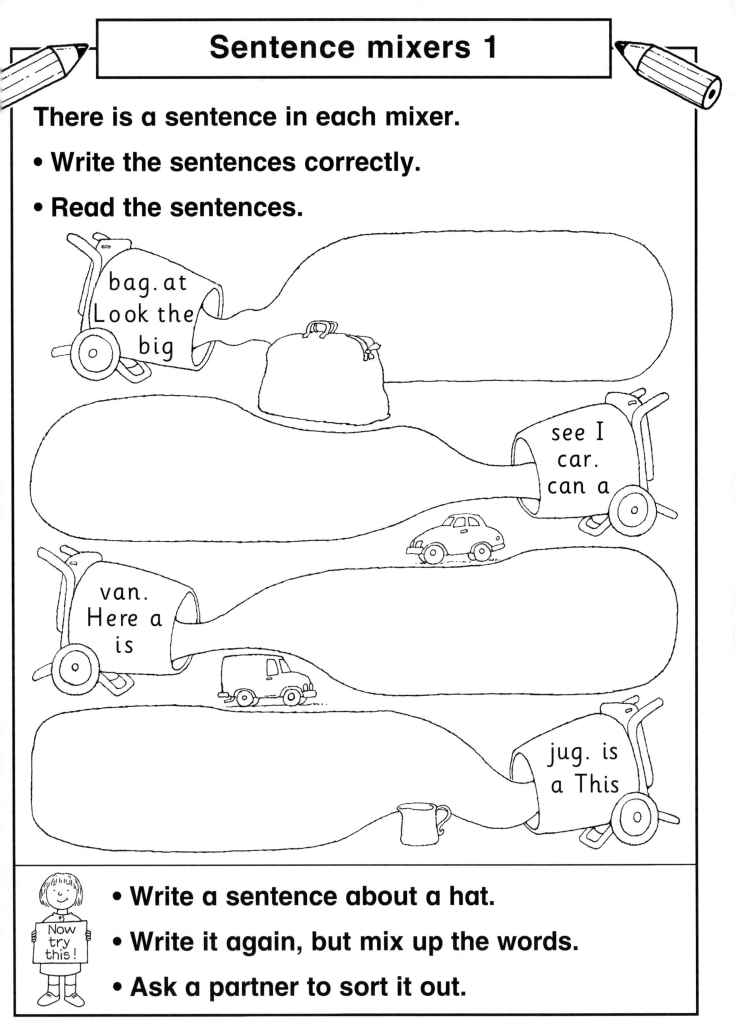

- **Write a sentence about a hat.**

- **Write it again, but mix up the words.**

- **Ask a partner to sort it out.**

Teachers' note Model the first example with the children, helping them to find the first and last word in the sentence.

Developing Literacy
Sentence Level Year R
© A & C Black

Sentence mixers 2

There is a sentence in each mixer.

- **Write the sentences correctly.**

- **Read the sentences.**

a have pig.big We

like I hat. Pat's

bed. is in Ted

sum. a did Mum

2+2=4

- **Write a sentence about a dog.**

- **Write it again, but mix up the words.**

- **Ask a partner to sort it out.**

Now try this !

Teachers' note Model the first example with the children, helping them to find the first and last word in the sentence.

Developing Literacy
Sentence Level Year R
© A & C Black

Sentence dominoes: set 1

He	She
The	It
Dad	Mum
I	You
is	are
was	were
went	can
play.	like

Teachers' note Photocopy this and pages 46 and 47, glue them on to card and cut out the dominoes. To make the game simpler, use fewer dominoes, ensuring that those chosen can be used to make sentences.

Developing Literacy
Sentence Level Year R
© A & C Black

Sentence dominoes: set 2

played	playing
go	going
likes	plays
goes	chips.
football.	cold
hot	out.
away.	come
coming	raining.

Teachers' note (Continued from page 45.) Deal the dominoes. The children take turns to lay down a domino. The first must have a word which begins with a capital letter. The second child adds a domino which would make grammatical sense in a sentence. Continued on page 47.

**Developing Literacy
Sentence Level Year R
© A & C Black**

sweets.	to
school.	the
the	the
park.	to
to	bed.
home.	at
my	day.
a	a

Teachers' note (Continued from page 46.) The third child adds another domino. If it has a full stop, it ends the sentence and the fourth child begins a new one. If a player has no suitable domino with which to continue or end a sentence, he or she misses a turn. The winner is the first to use up all his or her dominoes.

Developing Literacy
Sentence Level Year R
© A & C Black

What do they have?

What do they have?

• **Write the sentences.**

I have a
_____.

_____

_____

_____

ball   bag   mop   car

What do you have?

• **Draw a picture.**

• **Write a sentence.**

Now try this!

Teachers' note Introduce the activity by asking the children, in turn, to hold up various classroom items, one at a time, and asking them to give a sentence which says what they have. Write their sentences.

Developing Literacy
Sentence Level Year R
© A & C Black

Who does it?

- **Look at the pictures.**
- **Write the names.**
- **Read the sentences.**

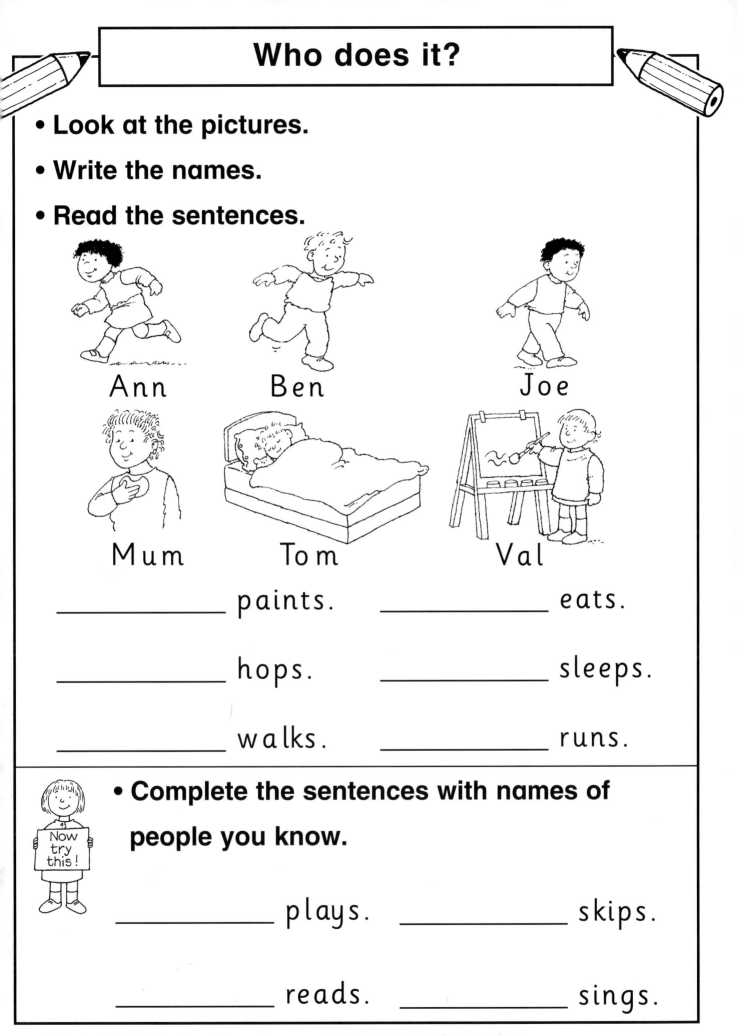

Ann   Ben   Joe

Mum   Tom   Val

_____ paints.   _____ eats.

_____ hops.   _____ sleeps.

_____ walks.   _____ runs.

- **Complete the sentences with names of people you know.**

Now try this!

_____ plays.   _____ skips.

_____ reads.   _____ sings.

Teachers' note To introduce the activity, read the names of the people shown on the activity sheet and ask the children what each person does. As an additional extension activity, the children could find sentences in simple story books which describe what people do. They could read them to a partner, then ask them to make a sentence saying what the character does.

**Developing Literacy
Sentence Level Year R
© A & C Black**

49

Hide and seek

- **Look at the pictures.**
- **Write the missing words.**
- **Read the sentences.**

Abby hid _____

Ali _____

John _____

Pip _____

by the wall.

in the tree.

under the mat.

in the cot.

under the bed.

Meg _____

- **Draw your friends playing hide and seek.**

  Where did they hide?

- **Write sentences.**

Now try this!

Teachers' note During the introductory session, the children could play 'hide and seek' with dolls or teddies which they hide. They could ask one another questions about where the dolls or teddies hid; the answers should be in sentences.

Developing Literacy
Sentence Level Year R
© A & C Black

Patch's day

- **Look at the picture story.**
- **Write the missing words.**
- **Read the story.**

Word-bank

opens
has
goes
chews

one eye   a walk   a drink   a bone

Patch opens _____ .

Patch has _____ .

Patch goes for _____ .

_____ .

- **What does Patch do next?**
- **Draw the next picture.**
- **Write a sentence.**

Now try this!

Teachers' note Read the activity sheet with the children, asking them to look at the pictures. Can they find the words in the box which say what Patch is doing?

Developing Literacy
Sentence Level Year R
© A & C Black

In the park

- **Look at the picture story.**
- **Write the missing words.**

Word-bank

is
are
play
feed

the swings   the park   trees   ducks

This is _____ .

There are _____

in _____ .

We can play on _____

_____ .

- **Read the story.**
- **Draw the next picture.**
- **Write a sentence.**

Now try this!

Teachers' note Discuss the pictures with the children: ask them to describe each one and to read the words beneath it. What could they add to those words to make a sentence about the picture?

Developing Literacy
Sentence Level Year R
© A & C Black

There was an old lady

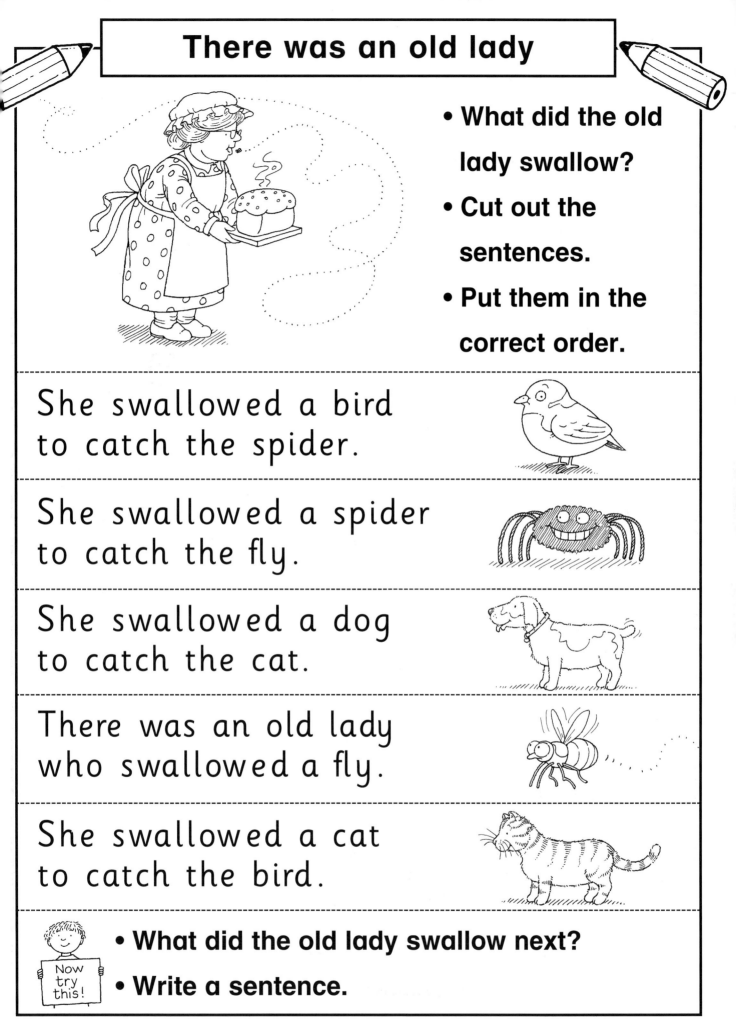

- **What did the old lady swallow?**
- **Cut out the sentences.**
- **Put them in the correct order.**

She swallowed a bird to catch the spider.

She swallowed a spider to catch the fly.

She swallowed a dog to catch the cat.

There was an old lady who swallowed a fly.

She swallowed a cat to catch the bird.

Now try this!

- **What did the old lady swallow next?**
- **Write a sentence.**

Teachers' note Read aloud the rhyme about the old lady who swallowed a fly, inviting the children to join in as you re-read it. Read it again, stopping before the name of each animal, which the children can predict. Ask them to name, in order, the animals which the old lady swallowed.

Developing Literacy
Sentence Level Year R
© A & C Black

53

Missing middles

- **Fill in the spaces.**

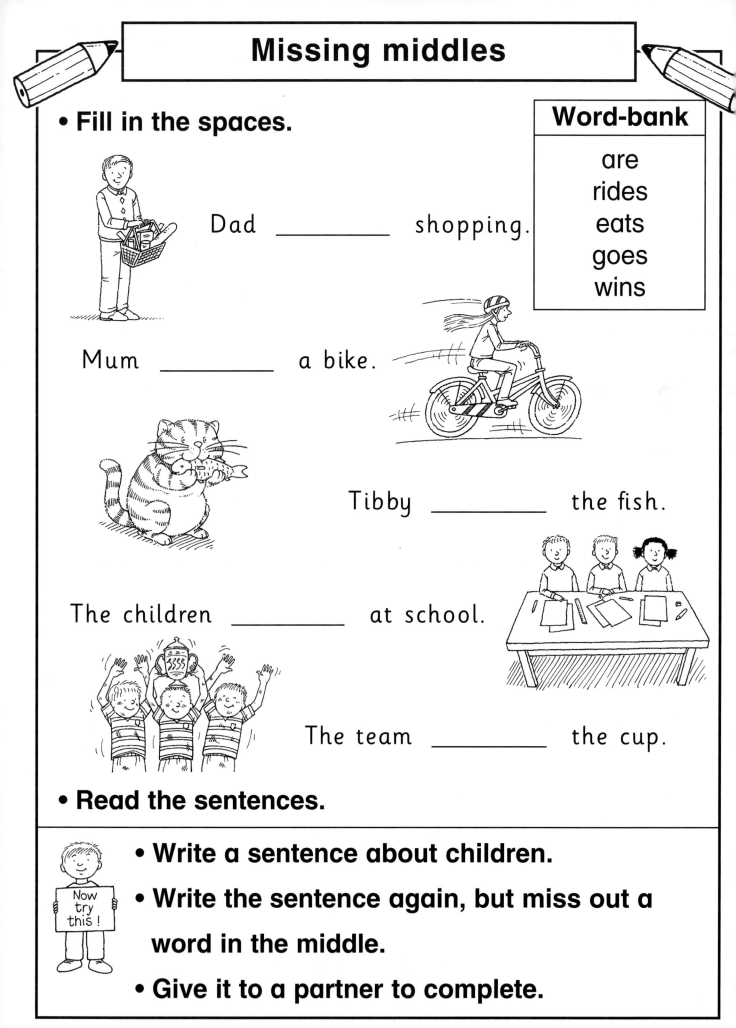

Dad _____ shopping.

Mum _____ a bike.

Tibby _____ the fish.

The children _____ at school.

The team _____ the cup.

- **Read the sentences.**

Now try this !

- **Write a sentence about children.**
- **Write the sentence again, but miss out a word in the middle.**
- **Give it to a partner to complete.**

Teachers' note Model the first example with the children. Can they think of a word or words with which to complete the sentence? Ask them to read it, filling in the gap with those words. Does it make sense? Does it describe the picture? Encourage them to try other words in the space.

**Developing Literacy
Sentence Level Year R
© A & C Black**

54

Sam		his cat.
He		his friend.
He sat		the chair.
The mat is		the door.
Lee has a		.
There is a		on the floor.
	won the race.	
	can swim.	

Teachers' note This is a game for three or four players. Photocopy this and pages 56 and 57 on to card and cut out the sentence strips and word cards. Place the sentence strips in a pile face down. Continued on page 56.

**Developing Literacy
Sentence Level Year R
© A & C Black**

Bob ____ his mum.

Rani ____ her dog.

She walked ____ the woods.

There was sand ____ the beach.

We saw a ____ .

I lost my ____ .

____ did well.

____ looked for a pen.

Teachers' note (Continued from page 55.) Deal the word cards face up. The children take a sentence strip from the pile, turn it over and read it together. The first child puts a word card in the space on the sentence strip, if he or she has one which makes sense there. If not, the next player has a turn, and so on. Continued on page 57.

Developing Literacy
Sentence Level Year R
© A & C Black

Missing word: word cards

feeds	likes	on	by
mouse	mat	She	He
loves	hugs	into	on
snake	book	Pam	Ben
sees	in	kite	penny
Bip	May	meets	to
crab	fish	rat	flag

Teachers' note (Continued from page 56.) Once a sentence strip is completed, the children take another and continue as before. The winner is the player who uses up all his or her cards first; if the game finishes because no suitable words are left, the winner is the one with the fewest cards.

**Developing Literacy
Sentence Level Year R**
© A & C Black

My name

- **Write your name on the label.**

_____

Names begin with a capital letter!

- **Write your name in each sentence.**

- **Read the sentences.**

- **Draw a picture for each sentence.**

_____ went

to school.

_____ sang

a song.

Mum waved

to _____ .

Now try this!

- **Read your work with a partner.**

  Are your answers the same?

  Why not?

Teachers' note During the introductory sesion, talk to the children about names; what do they notice about the first letter of a name?

Developing Literacy
Sentence Level Year R
© A & C Black

Names of other children

- **Give each child a name.**
- **Write their names in the boxes.**

- **Write the children's names in the sentences.**
- **Read the sentences.**

_____ has long hair.

_____ has glasses.

_____ has a dress.

_____ has a cat.

Remember the capital letter.

Now try this!

- **Draw your friend.**
- **Write your friend's name.**
- **Write a sentence about your friend.**

Teachers' note Encourage the children to read one another's names on books, displays, notices and labels around the classroom. Ask them to write one another's names. The owners of the names can check them.

**Developing Literacy
Sentence Level Year R
© A & C Black**

Hidden names

There are words hidden in the picture.

• Colour the shapes which have people's names in them.

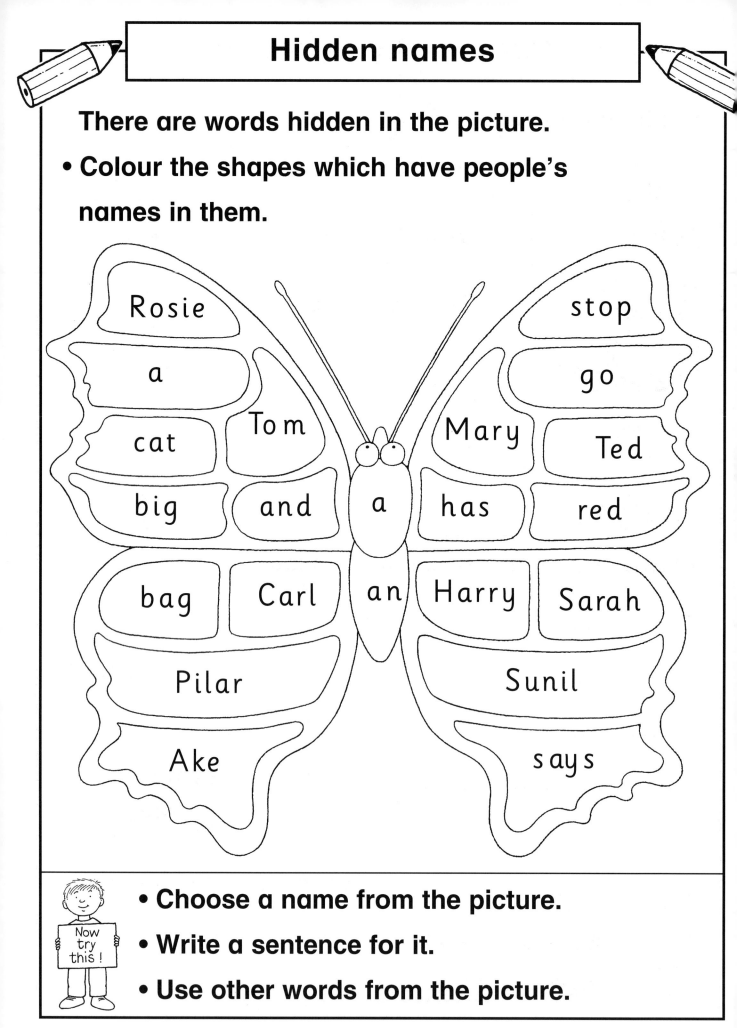

Rosie a cat big Tom and a Mary has stop go Ted red bag Carl an Harry Sarah Pilar Sunil Ake says

• **Choose a name from the picture.**
• **Write a sentence for it.**
• **Use other words from the picture.**

Now try this !

Teachers' note To introduce the activity, ask how the children can tell which words are names.

60

Developing Literacy
Sentence Level Year R
© A & C Black

Nursery rhyme names

• **Join the names to the characters.**

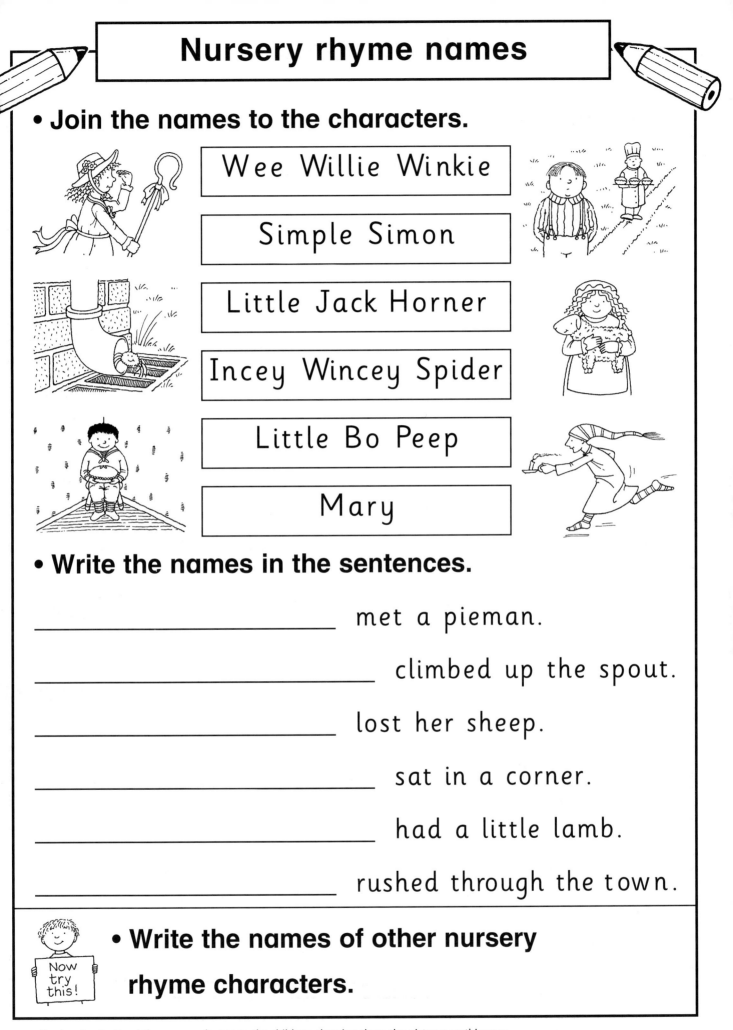

| Wee Willie Winkie |
| Simple Simon |
| Little Jack Horner |
| Incey Wincey Spider |
| Little Bo Peep |
| Mary |

• **Write the names in the sentences.**

_____ met a pieman.

_____ climbed up the spout.

_____ lost her sheep.

_____ sat in a corner.

_____ had a little lamb.

_____ rushed through the town.

• **Write the names of other nursery rhyme characters.**

Now try this!

Teachers' note Read the nursery rhymes to the children, showing them the pictures on this page and introducing the term 'character'. With the children, read the names of the characters and ask them if they can remember what each of them did in the rhymes.

Developing Literacy
Sentence Level Year R
© A & C Black

Sorting the post

- ## Sort the post.

- ## Match the letters to the people.

Goldilocks

Hansel and Gretel

Old King Cole

Pinocchio

Mother Goose

- ## Write these people's names.

Now try this!

Your mum _____

Your teacher _____

A singer _____

Teachers' note As an introduction, show the children rhymes and stories in which the characters on this page appear. What happens in them? The children could prepare for the extension activity at home by finding out how to spell their mother's name and a singer's name. Encourage them to find out the spelling of their teacher's name for themselves, asking where they will look.

Developing Literacy
Sentence Level Year R
© A & C Black

I

You can use $\boxed{\text{I}}$ instead of your name.

It is a capital letter.

- **Copy** I̲ ̲I̲ ̲I̲ ̲_____

- **Write** $\boxed{\text{I}}$ **in the sentences.**

____ am a baby.

____ like bones.

____ eat grass.

____ can fly.

____ bite.

____ live in the sea.

- **Write sentences with** $\boxed{\text{I}}$ **for these:**

Now try this!

Teachers' note Introduce the activity with a riddle. Can the children think of something which belongs to them but which other people use more than they do? Talk to them about yourself, using sentences which contain your name instead of 'I'. Ask what you should have said instead of your name.

**Developing Literacy
Sentence Level Year R
© A & C Black**

Using 'I'

- **Write your name in these sentences.**

_____ can sing.

_____ likes school.

_____ plays games.

_____ is great!

- **Write the sentences again.**

  Write `I` **instead of your name**

  > You sometimes have to change another word too.

_____

_____

_____

_____

- **Circle any other words which you changed.**

Now try this !

- **Write other sentences using your name.**

- **Write them again, but change your name to** `I` **.**

Teachers' note Talk to the children about yourself, using sentences which contain your name instead of 'I', writing the sentences down as you say them. Ask how you should say each sentence, writing the new sentences using 'I'. Which words were changed? The children should notice a change in the verb (although the term is not used here).

Developing Literacy
Sentence Level Year R
© A & C Black